WINDFALLS

MACMILLAN AND CO., Limited
LONDON · BOMBAY · CALCUTTA · MADRÀS
MELBOURNE

THE MACMILLAN COMPANY
NEW YORK · BOSTON · CHICAGO
DALLAS · ATLANTA · SAN FRANCISCO

THE MACMILLAN COMPANY
OF CANADA, LIMITED
TORONTO

WINDFALLS

STORIES, POEMS, AND PLAYS

BY

SEAN O'CASEY

MACMILLAN AND CO., LIMITED
ST. MARTIN'S STREET, LONDON
1934

COPYRIGHT

PREFACE

How I enjoyed the glory that was mine when something I had written first appeared in print! It was an article criticizing the educational policy in Ireland sponsored by Mr. Augustine Birrell, and the article appeared in a paper called *The Nation*, then edited by L. P. O'Ryan, who afterwards, I think, became Editor or Assistant Editor of the *Daily Herald*. I remember sending the paper in which the article appeared to a Protestant pastor for whom I had a deep fondness, and from whom I expected great praise and many words of encouragement, but the comment he made was a dead silence. Venturing, some weeks later, to ask him what he thought of it, he placed a hand gently on my shoulder and shocked me, saying, " The man who wrote that article, John, is a traitor, and ought to be in jail."

Many hot and weary days of activities in various National and Labour Organizations

followed. This was the time before the symbol
of Irish Republicanism had blossomed out into
the now well-known flags of green and white
and orange, but was represented by little tiny
bows of these colours worn by the stewards in
charge of the gatherings held in the Mansion
House or in the Rotunda, to celebrate the
memories and deeds of Wolfe Tone or of Robert
Emmet. Finally came the crash of the guns
in the Great War, and England's hurried and
agitated recruiting campaign in Ireland calling
on Irishmen of goodwill to go out and fight a
fight for little Catholic Belgium. Then " The
Grand Oul' Dame Britannia " was written,
printed as a " nix job " by friendly printers, and
circulated among the various National Societies.
Many others followed, all of which have gone
down into the limbo of forgotten things. But
I often wish that they were alive again, for
buried in them are a wild joy and a savage
bitterness that I shall never know again.
This was the time when the members of
the I.R.A. were oiling their guns, and in
almost every Irish Catholic home the Blessed
Virgin with the Child on her lap, and Jesus
hanging on the Cross, gave their messages
from green and white and orange frames;
while England went on cooing to herself

that hanging was the wisest way to satisfy the Irish.

A girl's fair face and charm of manner lured me from hanging around under the Irish tri-colour and the red banner of Labour, and first forced my feet in the way that led to a fuller understanding of Literature and Art. She was a child of Mary, gentle, patient, and generous. Commonplace in her Catholicism, she listened in a wonderful way to my reading of Shelley, Shaw, Milton, and even Schopenhauer; she heard with glistening eyes all that I said, took pride in all that I wrote, and diligently searched for beauty in many a shabby verse. Her influence appears in all written in the section which I have called the " First Fall."

The verses in the section called " Second Fall " were written in recent years, and the three short stories were an effort to get rid of some of the bitterness that swept into me when the Abbey Theatre rejected *The Silver Tassie*. The two One-Act Sketches were written when funds were low, to bring in a little money, but no attempt was made to market them, and so they shiver among the unemployed.

CHALFONT ST. GILES
1934

CONTENTS

FIRST FALL

SECOND FALL

A FALL FROM AN IRISH TREE

CONTENTS

FALLS IN A HIGH WIND

A FALL IN A GENTLE WIND

FALLS IN AN IDLE WIND

x

FIRST FALL

WISDOM AND LIFE

Wisdom is ofttimes nearer when we stoop than when we soar.

THE senatorial seers that pave
With obstacles the People's way,
And shatter hopes of ages till
Poor life regrets her tim'rous day;
Half spending life in building words
Till hair is scant and beards are grey,
Then spending all the rest of life
To take the pile of words away.
But surging life, in spite of these,
Still holds her everlasting sway,
And manifests her wisdom in
The glorious tune of children's play.

Poor precious priests with passion strive
Desires of flesh to overthrow,
And try to quench the flaming sun
In tiny flakes of sacred snow;
But clouds of sin and fear are chang'd
To rosy mists by love's warm glow,
And sober priests give place to Pan
Where thickets shade and blossoms blow;

3

WISDOM AND LIFE

His piping soothes the maid, and she
Yields to her lover's claims, and lo,
The god gives here a child of joy,
And yonder gives a child of woe.

Mind-curtain'd dons who preach success
And gold are life's most useful things—
Engrafting on the carrion crow
Rich plumage from the angels' wings,—
And teach the crowd to leap where'er
The pendulum of Judas swings,
Till man is like a dying tree
To which the poison'd fungus clings:
But new-born life, far distant still,
O'er Time's flower-crowded meadow springs,
To bring to man the wine of joy,
Press'd from the songs the poet sings.

A WALK WITH EROS

Oh, love is ever, ever old,
As love is ever young,
Extending from man's heart to all
The stars in heaven flung;
A song that's ever singing, yet
A song that's never sung.

When gentle Summer Breezes blow,
When Wintry winds are keen,
The sparkling frost or blooming flowers
Present a glorious scene—
When you and I walk arm in arm,
And Eros strolls between.

Spring's youthful song and Summer's
Full chorus, loud and clear;
Sad Autumn's pensive whisper,
Or Winter's silence drear,
Are never ending anthems
To love's enchanted ear.

And tho' the rosy god be blind,
His love-born visions show

A WALK WITH EROS

To all beneath his spell a world
Of colour, life, and glow,
Where every ebbing wave of thought
Brings but a fuller flow.

When Spring pours out her wine of life
Upon the frozen ground,
Then Nature frees her limbs that were
In Winter garments bound;
And when we hear the step of life,
Our hearts thrill at the sound.

And as the sun's rays brighter grow,
The trees in coy distress,
Make haste in foliag'd drapery
Their long bare limbs to dress,
Before Spring's ardent glance ashamed
Of their bold nakedness.

The gold laburnum, drooping o'er
The lilac's purple head—
Each fondly leaning close to each,
As if they had been wed,
Their purple, yellow blossoms fruits
Of Spring's sweet bridal bed.

Then Cybele sifts the gleaming gold
From Earth's broad-breasted mines,
And soon along the hedges green
We see the glorious signs
Of her hard work, in multitudes
Of golden dandelions.

A WALK WITH EROS

One day, when morn's half-open'd eyes
Were bright with Spring's sunshine—
My hand was clasp'd in yours, dear love,
And yours were clasp'd in mine—
We bow'd as worshippers before
The queenly celandine.

Mass'd in the meadow's outspread breast,
The yellow cowslips seem,—
Rous'd by the Sun to manifest
A richer golden gleam—
To our dull heavy west'rn eyes,
An Oriental dream.

The daisies breaking through the sod,
With spring-born strength endow'd,
Come pushing, like wild children, in
A snowy, panting crowd,
Too lovely to be humble, and
Too simple to be proud.

One eve, beneath a silver beech,
We saw a violet blue,
That seem'd to lift her gentle head,
To say something to you—
And you caress'd the lovely flower,
And I admir'd it too.

The chestnut blooms, like waxen lights,
On Nature's altar shone,
Till Spring's full choir had sung their hymn,
Had paus'd and pass'd and gone;

A WALK WITH EROS

Then Time, with steady hands, these lights
Extinguish'd, one by one.

How often, as we saunter'd through
Some blossom-broider'd lane,
We wonder'd if eventful life
Had most of loss or gain;
And ask'd if life evolv'd her best
From happiness or pain.

And when the hawthorn's gen'rous bloom
Was sprinkled everywhere,
Upon a bough, whose slender strength
Its blooms could hardly bear,
With crimson-tinted breast, we saw
A robin perching there.

The light of fond acquaintance seem'd
To twinkle in his eye—
As if he often watch'd before
When we went passing by—
Perhaps he knew the power of love
As well as you or I.

One shaded eve you loosen'd
Your mass of rich brown hair,
And stood before a white-thorn tree,
Half timid of my stare—
Your face like a sweet red rose
That had swiftly blossom'd there.

The world seem'd made of happiness
When we sat side by side;

A WALK WITH EROS

Hemm'd in by anxious trees that sought
Each fond embrace to hide;
Till night had pitch'd his tent, and gave
A shelter, deep and wide.

And how we talk'd of days that were,
And then of days to come;
When Certainty spoke loud and fast,
And Doubt was stricken dumb,
The love beats of our hearts like strokes
On a distant martial drum.

Here on my shoulder, fondly still,
Your sunny head at rest,
While my rough hand within your own
You silently caressed;
And I, with ravish'd eyes, admir'd
The blossoms of your breast.

Beneath the trees when raindrops fell,
Like searching drops of dew,
We scann'd the sky's long, gloomy face
For op'ning eyes of blue—
As you sat close to me, my love,
And I sat close to you.

Ah, how we tried to hold the hours,
As each one hurried past!
And how they laugh'd as we complain'd
That each went by too fast;
And each one murmur'd as he went,
That all things end at last.

9

A WALK WITH EROS

And how we felt as we sat close,
Deeper desires arise,
That you received with welcome coy,
And I with glad surprise;
And how we watch'd love's hunger-light
Gleam from each other's eyes.

Then when on your fair neck we saw
A red-coat lady-bird,
Seeking access to your white breast,
How your trembling hand demurr'd,
And replac'd her in the grasses
That the breezes gently stirr'd.

How full of life the moments as
We watch'd the sunset red,
Or gave a welcome to the moon
When she came out instead;
And sweeter than the words we spoke
Were the sweet words left unsaid.

Ah, love is joy that is to come,
And love is joy that's fled;
A tale well told in which best thoughts
Have all been left unsaid;
A book young life is reading,
And a book old life has read.

Great Nature paints the forms of life
In reckless light and shade;
Here flowers are bursting into bloom,
There flowers begin to fade;

A WALK WITH EROS

And death could not be closer to
The corn first in the blade.

Man hastens with the life that comes,
Or with the life that goes,
And schools of thought display to life
Their banner-waving shows,
Though he who knows not knows as much
As he who says he knows.

In a tiny church for a death-deaf man,
A tiny bell is toll'd;
While laughing youth thinks life did well
To exile one so old
From the fields whom the buttercups have clad
In rich, silken cloth of gold.

With filmy wings outspread like sails,
A fleet of tiny bees
Seek out the harbours of the flowers
That dot the meadow seas,
Then carry to their citied hives
Their honey argosies.

Cornfields, like waving hair of girls,
Dance in a golden maze;
Each, like a coquette, here and there,
A scarlet bow displays,
Wherever in the rip'ning corn
The crimson poppies blaze.

We listen to the cows that low,
Watch those that chew the cud;

A WALK WITH EROS

Or the young lambs that gaily frisk,
Youth's vigour in their blood;
Or in the hedge the goat that seeks
The tender bramble bud.

Ah, love's a flower that withers and
A flower that ever blooms;
A shadow over reason that
The soul of man illumes;
A wreath of whitest roses and
A bunch of sable plumes.

'Tis joy to turn our backs upon
The city's surly frown,
To see sweet Nature's smile increase,
All scornful of the town:
To see life looking wanton, like
A girl's hair tumbling down.

Those cattle and that speckl'd thrush,
The redly gleaming sun,
The sea, that spider waiting there
In web so finely spun;
All that are living and the dead,
Are but a mighty one.

But you and I, dear love, are one,
As those can never be;
Like flowing currents mingling in
An undivided sea:
So I am lost in you, my love,
And you are lost in me.

12

A WALK WITH EROS

When in the gathering silence sweet
That gives a fond embrace
To evening's gentle form, and gives
A kiss to her soft face,
We wander back the way we came,
With slow and reverent pace.

And after summer's whirling dance
All Nature's strength is sped,
Each flower and leaf show wearily
A faint and bending head;
And breezes sigh for that long rest
Found only with the dead.

How timidly you clung to me,
As if your fear to share,
When we march'd home 'neath dripping skies,
In thunder-heated air,
Whenever flash'd across our eyes
The lightning's sudden glare.

How fair you were in your white dress,
With borders bright of blue,
Like a mass of snowy hawthorn,
With the speedwell peeping through,
And a rakish Tam O' Shanter
On the rich brown head of you!

When we lay beneath the foliage
Of a gently screening oak,
And sank to pensive silence as
The beauty round us spoke;

A WALK WITH EROS

And our surging senses slumber'd as
Our slumbering souls awoke.

Then our life was like a tranquil,
Yet a swiftly flowing stream;
Then our life of mingling joy made all
The rest of life a dream.
While all the world was darkness,
Where we were was all agleam.

Like a sky-concealing forest,
Fragrant with the rich perfumes
Pour'd in streams of ardent breathing
From thick clust'ring hosts of blooms;
While the life forgotten, carried
On its life of frets and fumes;

Were the days and all the moments
As we wandered to and fro;
When our bodies were oblivious
To life's law of come and go;
And our minds ignor'd life's question,
Asking all men, yes or no.

Then sweet Beauty spoke beside us—
And her voice was music rare,—
Saying in a plaintive whisper
That if men would only dare
To seek to see my form, he'd see
Me standing everywhere.

14

A WALK WITH EROS

In strength of solitary trees,
In the close-commingling sod;
On the sun-kissed hills of Sion,
In the shadowy Land of Nod;
In the mind of a son of Satan,
Or the mind of a child of God.

I am truly bread from heaven,
For the soul's tormenting need;
Child of man and child of woman,
Very God of God, indeed;
The quick seed that forms the blossom,
And the flower that bears the seed.

And we saw God's fingers weaving
All the grandeur of the scheme;
And we saw His face reflected
In the mirror of the stream:
Tho' we knew our souls were shaping
Gorgeous shadows of a dream.

Sens'd the savour of His garments
In the shaking grasses long;
Heard the chanting of His Angels
In the thrushes' thrilling song;
And our souls join'd in the chorus
Of the dream-created throng.

And we saw His arm tremendous
Gently shake the trembling leaf;
Saw man drape the robe of Justice
Round the shoulders of a thief;

A WALK WITH EROS

Saw the child of Beauty leaping
In the gloomy womb of grief.

And we felt the power that fashion'd
All the lovely things we saw,
That created all the murmur
Of an everlasting law,
Was a hand of force and beauty,
With an eagle's tearing claw!

And we felt the mind that made us,
Made us in and out of tune,
Made of life a certain sorrow,
Hidden in uncertain boon;
Like a glowing picture by a
Hand unsteady brought to ruin.

Dark Winter mounts dead Summer's throne,
And strips her regal chair
Of th' last blossoms Autumn kind
Had left to linger there;
And flings them, scornful, to the winds,
Their kindred's fate to share.

She sits in silent solitude,
Wrapp'd in her robe of gloom;
Hemm'd with a million sparkling gems
Of frost's white crystal spume—
Like spectral shades of Summer flowers,
New risen from the tomb.

Love flees the Wintry moon, and rests
Where shades her visions dim;

A WALK WITH EROS

And man and maiden senses sweet
With glowing raptures swim,
With breast to breast, and lip to lip,
And limb caressing limb.

When we come back to city streets,
Drab-fac'd and gable-spir'd,
Eros' visions lose their beauty,
Where the herds of men are byr'd;
For 'tis only in the city that
His tireless feet are tir'd.

In the dust-clad streets, thro' all the
Lumb'ring hours 'tween dawn and dark;
'Mid the greedy roar of traffic,
In the city's shrinking park;
He can never hear the blackbird,
Nor the wild song of the lark.

Here Honour's bastard sister gilds
The human things that crawl;
Here the many are neglected,
And the few are all in all;
Here the worth of goods is great, and
Here the worth of life is small.

Passing sheep, lost to the country,
With a mournful cadence bleat;
Or a herd of meek-ey'd cattle
Amble slowly down the street,
Braving death, that man, their brother,
May remain to live and eat.

17

A WALK WITH EROS

A curse upon the state of life,
That life for long has led,
For life oft seeks escape from life,
By seeking out the dead;
Not that life of life was weary,
But because life needed bread.

Here Statesmen, with sly hands and slick,
Seek out and deftly drape
With stars and richly colour'd gowns,
Blood brothers to the ape;
Here creeds sell womanhood, and make
The marriage vows a rape.

The days with gentle Mary spent,
Like lightning flashes sped;
The hours without her seem to stand
All motionless and dead,
And grin with age-worn faces grim,
Before they move ahead.

Our days like fragrant petals fall
From life's decaying rose;
And falling, sadden all the rest
That still the flower enclose,
Till all are gone, and death life's stem
To mystic darkness throws.

Let those who will dream heaven's dreams,
Or fear a pictur'd hell,
Who answer Nature's outcries with
The Church's blatant bell:

A WALK WITH EROS

But we can worship only where
Sweet Nature's beauties dwell.

Where gen'rous Nature's hands, untir'd,
Rich feasts of colour spread;
And souls, esthetic, lustful lie
In beauty's blossom'd bed;
And gaze on th' illumin'd scroll,
Where Nature's lore is read.

Here Nature's life with Nature's life
In wanton glee conflicts;
Where sky and trees, and flowers and bees,
In amorous order mix,
Undaunted by the gloomy shade
Of the dolorous crucifix.

Dewdrops that gem the hedge, or those
That sparkle at our feet;
The lark, hilarious, rising swift,
The new-born day to greet;
The maiden flowers that shyly ope
Their fragrant faces sweet.

Here lilies of the valley, shy,
Bend low their pendant bells;
The tow'ring foxglove, purple-dress'd,
With conscious vigour swells;
And every diff'rent flower its own
Sweet tale of beauty tells.

A WALK WITH EROS

'Mid buzz of bees and song of birds,
Veil'd in a sky of blue,
Green-edg'd with foliag'd lace, we learn
The lore that first man knew—
As you sit close to me, my love,
And I sit close to you.

CHOSEN LIFE

You have not chosen me, but I have chosen you.

GREAT is a Solomon or a Caesar great,
In the robes of a nation dressed;
Or a saint who has climb'd to the edge of the stars
That encircle the Virgin's breast;
Or a soul singing on in the way of life,
Finding all a gigantic jest;
Or a maiden wrapp'd in a swoon of joy,
In the arms of her lover press'd;
But grander and prouder and happier far,
And dearer than these to me,
Is the passionate heart of the amorous flower
As she waits for the passing bee.

Grand is the great bard playing his harp
In a wail or a chant of glee;
Or a patriot spilling his heart's best blood,
That his country may be free;
Or a pontiff binding and loosing souls
From the throne of a world-wide see;
Or a rich man op'ning the gates of life
With the power of a golden key;

CHOSEN LIFE

But grander and fairer and finer far,
And dearer than these to me,
Are the gambols bright of a squirrel red
On the bough of a big beech tree.

The army, pulse of a nation's pride,
And shield of a nation's fear;
Busy raising the dead, giving sight to the blind,
And making the deaf to hear,
Till envious thought strikes down the flags,
And the victories disappear;
Then the officer's sword and the rifleman's gun
Flout the savage's club and spear;
Dearer and grander and prouder far,
And finer than these to me,
Is the daffodil's dance to the pipes of Pan,
In the wind on the wind-swept lea.

Grand are the red-clad men who ride
Swift steeds from a hunting stud,
While full-grown feminine flowers follow on,
With a few that are still in the bud;
While the fox flees on with the blood in his veins,
On fire in a panting flood,
Three gods looking down from their pearl-girt throne
Pronouncing the sport to be good:
But the gods have spoken enough—let them hear
A word from a sinner like me,
For the panting breast of the frightened fox
Is a terrible thing to see:—
Grander and greater and fairer far,
And dearer than these to me,

CHOSEN LIFE

Is the fragrant scent from the fragrant bloom,
On the white-headed hawthorn tree.

Fair is a fane whose sculptur'd stones
Stand still in a grand parade;
Or a colour'd joy where an artist with
A wonderful brush has play'd;
Or the trumpet peal of a tribune's tongue
That millions of minds has sway'd,
Or a steel-brained thing whose power the thoughts
Of millions of years have made;
But grander and fairer and prouder far,
And dearer than these to me,
Are the movements rare of a sea-bird's wings
Shadow'd soft in a mirror-like sea.

The Judge enthron'd high on the Book of the Law,—
A type of the Ancient of Days—
Looking down, with the sternness of Moses enrag'd,
On the criminal soul that he weighs,
His might treading down a poor soul that a Christ
Suffer'd hard on a cross to upraise,
Donning a soft mourning cap to give awe
To the dread formal words that he says;
True to self and to man, but a traitor to God
In the blasphemous prayers that he prays.
Oh dearer and grander and fairer far,
Far fairer than these to me,
Is the lark singing into the morn's hush'd ear,
Her wonderful song of glee.

SUNSHADOWS

When Spring's fair sun is climbing o'er the hills,
And morn is new,
Fresh gold upon the golden daffodils,
Rich gemm'd with dew;
And fragrance sweet from lovely violets blue,
Perfumes the air, I long to walk with you.

Or 'neath the hawthorn's deeply scented shade,
With you alone,
To revel in love's joys before they fade
From fulness grown;
To reap the harvest love has thickly sown,
And laugh at self-crown'd virtue on her throne.

Or ponder long beside the restless sea
Love's rosy schemes,
While doubt is symboliz'd to you and me
In seagulls' screams;
To sleep in hope's broad arms whose magic dreams
Robs life of truth, and makes life all it seems.

Or wond'ring at a river's dauntless flow,
Without a care,

SUNSHADOWS

Watching its rhythmic endless come and go,
Now here, now there;
Then asking why poor man should bless or swear
When fate's strong arm is raised to smite or spare.

Or, when sweet Summer's ardent arms outspread,
Entwin'd with flowers,
Enfold us like two lovers newly wed,
Thro' ravished hours;
Then sorrow, woe, and pain lose all their powers,
For each is dead, and joy and life are ours.

Or stroll along where timid lilac bloom
In clusters bend,
Or, hiding in the stilly twilight gloom,
Its blossoms send
Their fragrance sweet like mem'ries of a friend,
Who sought new life and, maybe, found the end.

When night advances thro' the sky with slow
And solemn tread,
The queenly moon looks down on life below
As if she read
Man's soul, and in her scornful silence, said,
All beautiful and happiest things are dead.

And when the stars in gleaming millions throng
The pendant skies,
They view the fight that goes against the strong,
Hear cheers and sighs,
Where armour'd greed smites right until she dies,
And madmen sit enthron'd on savage lies.

SUNSHADOWS

Where churches make a sacrament of gold;
And slavish schools
Teach life that life divine is dead and cold,
By creeds and rules,
Dulling the gleam of mankind's fairest jewels,
Crushing new thought 'neath herds of trampling fools.

Or stroll in Winter thro' the woods that were
In splendour spread
A day ago, but now are bleak and bare,
Silent and dead;
Save where the robin in his vest of red,
Pipes rebel tunes where other birds have fled.

Pale superstition paints her waning face
With gaudy hue,
And charms with fetters all the human race,
All, but the few:
Who fearless stand, and live the life that's true,
Tho' ston'd down to the dead, or rob'd in rue.

When life has reach'd her toilsome journey's end,
And looks behind,
She sees ten days were foes and one a friend,
Ten harsh, one kind;
That Justice ever was to Justice blind,
And wonders who the sorry plan designed.

THE GARLAND

No shining pearls from orient seas,
No wondrous sapphires brilliant blue,
Strung on a golden string could make
A garland rich enough for you.

Nor all the em'rald's glorious green,
And rubies rich in crimson hue,
Mix'd with the opal's glow could make
A garland rich enough for you.

But in the wood's deep shaded bower,
Where grow rare violets richly blue,
I'll gather all these gems of bloom,
And make a garland, love, for you.

Or wander where sweet roses blow,
Of gentle, fair, or flaming hue,
I'll gather all these gems of bloom,
And make a garland, love, for you.

With fragrant lilies of the vale,
Lac'd tenderly with morning dew,
I'll gather all these gems of bloom,
And make a garland, love, for you.

THE GARLAND

And golden celandines as well,
The perfum'd may and speedwell, too,
I'll gather all these gems of bloom,
And make a garland, love, for you.

Could I find flowers in far-off fields,
Fairer than all that ever grew,
I'd gather all those gems of bloom,
And make a garland, love, for you.

Ah, could I climb among the stars,
Gleaming in heaven's deepest blue,
I'd seize the brightest orbs of all,
To make a garland, love, for you!

THOUGHTS OF THEE

A thought came to me like a full-blown rose.

THRO' all the hours that life shall go,
Sweet hours or sad, hours swift or slow,
Each passing moment brings to me
Full blooming rose-like thoughts of thee.

The shaded woods where linnets throng,
The rich notes of the thrush's song,
The blackbird piping on a tree,
Are all sweet murmuring thoughts of thee.

The brook that kisses as it flows
Each flower that on its border grows,
Babbling its love, is—love to me—
A limpid, lovely thought of thee.

The dawn, casting night's robes away,
To wanton in the arms of day,
Blushing, her own fair charms to see,
Is morning's tender thought of thee.

When God the painter paints His dream,
And night's great orbs are all agleam,

THOUGHTS OF THEE

Time girdles dread eternity,
And gems her robe with thoughts of thee.

When ev'ning gently soothes to sleep
The weary day, and slumber deep
Enfolds each flower in copse and lea,
The silence breathes sweet thoughts of thee.

The celandine, the sensuous rose,
And every lovely flower that blows,
The scented bloom of hawthorn tree,
Are fragrant, incens'd thoughts of thee.

The heather, robing hillsides bare,
With glorious purple garments rare,
Broider'd with gorse-gold filagree,
Are purple, golden thoughts of thee.

Thro' all the hours that life shall go,
Sweet hours or sad, hours swift or slow,
Each passing moment brings to me
Full blooming rose-like thoughts of thee.

BONNIE MARY

Air: "Over the hills to Mary."

WHEN night's deep shadows darkly fall,
The moon breaks thro' the sombre thrall,
And then beneath her silver shawl,
I see the face of Mary.
And as I wander lonely here,
I lift my eyes to yon bright sphere,
And, joyous, know she shines as clear
To my dear winsome Mary.

Here as I stand beneath the trees,
Thro' which blows soft the evening breeze,
From life's clay house my spirit flees
In search of bonnie Mary.
Bright moon that shines so softly fair,
Bear swift my rapturous thoughts to where
Thy beams fall on the nut-brown hair
Of gentle winsome Mary.

Fair moon upon thy throne of blue,
Thy robe thy beams, thy gems the dew,
No orb of night can vie with you—
No colleen with my Mary.

31

BONNIE MARY

In loveliness she all transcends,
Enthron'd she reigns among my friends—
My deepest love begins and ends
With bonnie winsome Mary.

O Force eternal, Power divine,
By whom men live and planets shine,
With blessing bless this girl of mine,
My gentle winsome Mary!
With love for me her heart enflame,
Let all the joy that from love came
Since man first found for love a name,
Be shared with me and Mary!

SECOND FALL

GOLD AND SILVER WILL NOT DO

I GAZED into her blue eyes, and behold, she was as fair as an everlasting branch of appleblossom.

And I claimed her and laid hold of her love in the frowning face of others, who, frightened, fled and were scattered even as the dust scattereth before a wind that is strong.

They bowed in their pride before her, for they had many possessions, and proud confidence stiffened their bending.

They drowsily dropped at her feet trinkets of silver and trinkets of gold.

They touched her white breasts with the tops of their fingers, saying, calm in their pride: these fair things of silver and fair things of gold are for thee in return for the favours thy white body can give.

Round her white arms she fastened the trinkets of silver, encircled her neck with the trinkets of gold, and the gleam of the gold made her white bosom whiter than ever.

She smiled and was pleased, and she said: they are pleasant and fair, and they honour my loveliness.

I came quick, came running, stopping not till I came within a hand's breadth of her bosom. I looked at the silver encircling her arm, at the gold lying gay on her breast; then I lifted my eyes and looked into the eyes of the girl wearing silver and gold.

I gathered her close to my love in a song that dulled, as I sang, the gleaming of silver and gold.

She fondled the trinkets of silver and gold as she said: these are pleasant and fair and they honour the power of my beauty.

I answered and said: they are nought but some specks of fine dust that once fell from the luminous robe of the sun.

She looked down in sorrow, and questioned me, saying: what hast thou to give me if I leave these things that honour my loveliness, and mingle my life with the life that is thine?

And I gripped her arm till the checked blood
36

reddened its whiteness, and answered: I will
give thee love; I will give thee thoughts of care
and signs of sorrow; but at the beginning will
be love, and love shall be at the end thereof.

She answering said: these others promise me
many gifts, and their promises are good, for,
see, they have given me these things that are
fair, and that honour my loveliness. What
greater things than these hast thou to give if I
go to mingle my life with the life which is thine?

I answered and said: woman, whose fair form
is lovelier than the gentle shape of the rowan
tree, I will give thee heaviness of heart when
thou art absent from me, and a heavier heaviness
of heart when I am absent from thee; but at the
beginning will be love, and love shall be the end
thereof.

And lo, the others brought silks of proud
yellows and silks of crimson that were lovely
with grandeur of hue; and silks of blue and silks
of green that gleamed with rich quietness of
grace.
They bowed down before her, and proud
confidence stiffened their bending.
And they laid the silks of yellow and blue and
crimson and green at her feet.

And they murmured, saying: these shall be unto thee as scarves of beauty for thy neck and for thy breast, and as robes for thy fair and desirable body.

Then they fondled her white breasts and touched her white thighs and were with desire for the joys of her body.

They said unto the woman: the people shall stand still; they shall look on thee and stand still, and clap their hands because of thine own beauty, and because of the beauty of the things we have given unto thee.

The woman fondled the silks, gay as sun-coloured clouds in the sky, silks of yellow and green and of crimson and blue, and her heart followed after their richness and grace.

And she questioned me, saying: all these things are mine and much more for the asking: what givest thou unto me now, if I go, and what else shall be mine in the days that shall follow my going?

I answered and said: I will give thee my love, and my need of thee, now; and in the days that shall follow thy going, colours many times more wonderful than these colours that shine in this

silken loveliness of yellow and green and crimson
and blue; and I will bring thee more marvellous
things in bronze and in stone than even these
trinkets of silver and trinkets of gold.

The others jingled the gold on her breasts,
and laughed long and laughed wearily, saying:
he dreams: There is nothing to delight like
unto the things that we offer thee; for all the
joys of the world are revealed and are hid in
these silks, and in the trinkets of silver and
trinkets of gold.

And the woman gave ear to the words of the
others, and, turning, she questioned me, saying:
where shall I find, O dreamer, colours outshin-
ing the colours they give me, or grandeur in
bronze and in stone like the grandeur of silver
and gold?

O woman, who art fairer than an everlasting
branch of appleblossom, I answered, they are to
be found first in the deeper depths of thine own
heart and of thine own mind; and, afterwards, in
the depths of the hearts and the minds of the
poets.

Then the others murmured among themselves, saying: he dreams.

And they laughed long and laughed wearily,

saying unto the woman: he dreams. In a world well searched, there is nothing to be found more precious than these things we offer unto thee.

Then the womanhood in the woman trembled and fear came upon her.

And she gripped my arm and pressed it, saying: I listen; hasten to tell me then, what else, besides the things thou findest praise for, wilt thou give me, now, and in the days that shall follow my going?

I looked into the eyes of the maid; I pressed my hand over her breast, and answered, saying: beloved maiden, in whom are the seeds of life, and the battle of life, I will bring thee to where a child's cry shall hush thy laughter, and a child's laugh shall still thy weeping; and love shall be at the beginning and at the end thereof.

Then the others laughed long and loud and bitterly, saying: he dreams: and dreaming, hails sorrow as joy. Behold, we will cause thee to be surrounded with pleasure and sheltered with ease. Tenderly cushioned cars, gliding like gently flowing water, or rushing swiftly like a hurrying wind, shall bear thee from place to place, and none shall touch thee save those who come to serve. Go not with him who would

make of life a day of battle, and night a night of
care.

Then singing loose songs softly, they stretched
out their hands and began to unloosen her girdle.

And the woman in the maiden trembled
again, and she let the silks of crimson and green
and yellow and blue fall from her hands; and
she took the trinkets of silver from her arms,
and the trinkets of gold she took from her bosom
and they fell down on the silks of yellow and
green and crimson and blue.

And she stretched out her arms to me yearn-
ingly, saying: behold I have made my choice
and have chosen thee, and the things thou hast
to give me, and the things thou hast to show me,
where love is the beginning, and love is the
ending thereof.

And I struck away the hands that were un-
loosening her girdle, and tightened it again, that
I myself, with mine own hands, might loosen it
in an hour that was on its way. And I gathered
her in my arms, and pressed her mouth to my
mouth; and she was in nowise afraid, but pressed
me to her bosom.

And the others hastened, and gathered up the

trinkets of silver and trinkets of gold, and the silks of crimson and green and yellow and blue.

And they fled away and were scattered even as the dust scattereth before a wind that is strong.

THE DREAMER DREAMS OF GOD

THE Dreamer dreaming a dream gets God as a
comrade majestic, who walks with the Dreamer
at dawn of the day, and again in the cool of the
evening.

We hail Him as ours, for He is our friend,
and is one with the Dreamers for ever.

The sun is just a wee brooch in His breast;
The moon is a stone in the ring He is wearing;
The stars are the beads gleaming grand in
His robe, when the ev'ning has fallen.

We praise Him, for He is our friend, and is
one with the Dreamers for ever.

The sea is the pool where He bathes; His
gentle hand rippling the water
Upraises the waves that run back and away
in fear and confusion,
Crashing on to the coasts, tossing fiercely
afoam on the beaches;

43

And every ship cleaving a way through the waves is alert and atremble.

We praise Him, for He is our friend, and is one with the Dreamers for ever.

The lightning dividing the dark is a quick and calm flash from His eyes;
The thunder's the whisper of power in His voice speaking low with emotion.

We hail Him as ours, for He is our friend, and is one with the Dreamers for ever.

His hand that is mighty is slender and white as the slender and elegant hand of a beautiful maiden.
We see its soft touch in the calm yellow glow of the primrose,
The red in the white of the may,
And the bronzèd ton'd leaves of the trees in the Autumn.

We praise Him, for He is our friend, and is one with the Dreamers for ever.

He gives a glance down as we wake, and we see the girlish cool form of the morning;
He smiles; and the morn dances on in the gay virgin blue of the day-sky.

DREAMS OF GOD

We hail Him as ours, for He is our friend,
and is one with the Dreamers for ever.

He lights a great light in the eyes of the
Dreamer in colour,
He touches the lips of the Dreamer, brave
singer of songs,
And their visions glow into great gems on the
back and the breast,
On the sleeves, on the skirt, and the hem of
His garment.

He guides the firm hand of the Dreamer in
stone, and the stone
Blossoms into a beauty that God can acknow-
ledge and praise.

He touches the ear of the Dreamer in sound,
and the Dreamer plays sound into greatness,
And ears that are open hear God in His pride,
speaking out of His glory.

The cold-minded searching-ey'd Dreamer in
science holds on to God's hand, looks into His
face, and ever keeps asking Him questions; sits
still at His feet, and is learning.

We praise Him, for He is our friend, and is
one with the Dreamers for ever.

Beset by the laughter and malice of fools, the

DREAMS OF GOD

Dreamers climb on and climb up the white flaming steps of His throne, beset by the laughter and malice of fools.

We hail Him as ours, for He is our friend, and is one with the Dreamers for ever.

SHE WILL GIVE ME REST

My belov'd is sweet and fair and comely,
The poet's sadden'd gladness singing,
Like unto a rose's fragrance scenting
The bosom of the deep'ning dusk.
The mass'd mad whirl of the city's uproar,
Hammering out life's fierce ambitions,
Sinks to a murmur mingling with the
Song of her white hands clasp'd in mine.

Men of the market, busy with decimals,
Smother with spittle the glorious fancies
That flow from the brooding mind of God,
And are colour'd anew in the songs of the poets.
Apes who have stamped their blasted trademarks
Over the lyric-jewel'd zone of Venus,
And would stamp them, too, on the stars of God,
Or the moment's glory of a butterfly's wing,
Smother with spittle the glorious fancies
That flow from the brooding mind of God
Into the brooding mind of the poets.

Out of the clay of life's meanness and grandeur,
Here I am moulding wondering figures,

47

SHE WILL GIVE ME REST

And sending them out with blessing and cursing,
To dance a way through the hurrying throng;
Who, passing, gaze for an idle moment
At the strife sent forth from a poet's soul,
His flaming pain for a second shadow'd
In the soft, brown-gold of his lov'd one's hair.

Sick with the shame of the welcoming tumult
Given the crowd-lov'd vendors of tinsel,
Trying to fix their gilded dung-beads
On the breast of a Muse giving suck to the poets;
Tir'd of the dangerous peering into
Flame-images deep in the eyes of God,
I sink to rest for a breathless moment
On the cool, white, sheltering breast of a woman.

A FALL FROM AN IRISH TREE

THE GRAND OUL' DAME
BRITANNIA

Air: "Leather away with the wattle O."

AH, Ireland, sure, I'm proud of you,
Ses the Grand Oul' Dame Britannia,
To poor little Belgium thried an' true,
Ses the Grand Oul' Dame Britannia.
For ye don't believe the Sinn Fein lies
And ye know each Gael that for England dies,
'ill enjoy Home Rule in the clear blue skies,
Ses the Grand Oul' Dame Britannia.

Sure, it often made me proud blood boil,
Ses the Grand Oul' Dame Britannia,
When they tried to make out you were still disloyal,
Ses the Grand Oul' Dame Britannia,
But Redmond's prov'd to be good and great,
He's a pillar of the English State—
Who fears to speak of Ninety-Eight!
Ses the Grand Oul' Dame Britannia.

You want a pound or two from me,
Ses the Grand Oul' Dame Britannia,

OUL' DAME BRITANNIA

For your oul' Hibernian Academy?
Ses the Grand Oul' Dame Britannia.
But you know we've got the Huns to quell,
And we want the cash for shot and shell,
So your artists all can go to hell!
Ses the Grand Oul' Dame Britannia.

The Castle's now an althered place,
Ses the Grand Oul' Dame Britannia,
It's the Drawin' Room of the Irish Race,
Ses the Grand Oul' Dame Britannia;
John Redmond to the throne is bow'd
'Mid a frantic cheerin' Irish crowd—
God, it's like the days of Shane the Proud!
Ses the Grand Oul' Dame Britannia.

Oh, Johnny Redmond, you're the boy,
Ses the Grand Oul' Dame Britannia,
You're England's pride and you're Ireland's joy,
Ses the grand Oul' Dame Britannia;
For he went to France and he fac'd the Hun,
Then he turn'd round an' he fir'd a gun—
Faith, you should have seen the Germans run!
Ses the Grand Oul' Dame Britannia.

And Redmond now Home Rule has won,
Ses the Grand Oul' Dame Britannia,
And he's finish'd what Wolfe Tone begun,
Ses the Grand Oul' Dame Britannia;
Yet rebels through the country stalk,
Shoutin' "Sixty-Seven" an' "Bachelor's Walk"—

OUL' DAME BRITANNIA

Did ye ever hear such foolish talk!
Ses the Grand Oul' Dame Britannia.

Oh, Scholars, Hurlers, Saints, and Bards,
Ses the Grand Oul' Dame Britannia,
Come along an' list in the Irish Guards,
Ses the grand Oul' Dame Britannia;
Each man that treads on a German's feet,
Will be giv'n a parcel tied up neat,
Of a tombstone cross an' a windin' sheet,
Ses the Grand Oul' Dame Britannia.

FALLS IN A HIGH WIND

I WANNA WOMAN

JACK AVREEN was waiting for a girl to come and have a light little supper with him in his flat. Between half-past eight and nine she was to arrive, and it was now a quarter to nine. Any minute she might be here now, tossing all his emotions into a hot and exquisite whirl of uncertain anticipations. The packed bud of anticipation might burst into a rich-coloured realization to-night if he was careful enough. It wanted a little careful handling, that was all. A girl didn't come along to a man's flat for nothing. Sit down calmly together and sing hymns? Not damn well likely. He would have to move cannily to-night, though. Bring her along gradually. A hasty movement might frighten her and spoil everything. It would be maddening if she fought shy of it again. Like the night a week ago when she was with him here, and he hurried the pace on too suddenly. Everything was going grand, and if he only had

had the patience to spread the final fuss over
another half-hour or so, he'd have got her sure
—but no, he must try to rush things, and in ten
minutes she had her hat on saying she'd have to
go, and bidding him an agitated good-night.
Then for a week he had to bring her to a theatre,
to meals in public restaurants, and to walk re-
spectfully and respectably with her till he had
subdued her timidity into coming again to his
flat for a light supper and an hour or so of
secluded companionship. She was a Catholic
and that made it more difficult, though it
shouldn't, for plenty of Catholics were hot stuff
too. But Catholic or no Catholic, if he couldn't
get her going this time, he'd just shunt her off
finally about her business. She went too far
altogether without going far enough. It was a
bit thick to applaud desire till it was a passion
ready to overthrow everything, and then to
expect a sudden thought of shyness or fear to
trim it down to a cool-centred flame of torturing
self-control. Pandering to passion; playing
with passion, and then asking passion to behave
itself. She wouldn't get him to stop so easily
this time. When he saw that passion had filled
her with a wild, throbbing, and delicious confusion he would go on determinedly and exact
a full and perfect satisfaction out of her. She

could even do a faint if she liked; that wouldn't
lure him into any frightened, pitiful, or con-
scientious withdrawal. In fact a faintness would
make the job easier. When she weakened with
emotion, that was the time to hammer a job on
her. So long as she didn't start to yell. That
would make everything impossible. He remembered the last time she was with him here
how she started to yell when he tried to show
her how nice she'd look lying down stretched
out on the divan. The roars of her . . . let me
up . . . let me up . . . let me up! Pretence, the
whole of it. Imagine a girl, even a Catholic,
living in London all her life not knowing her
way about. The idea was stillborn. He would
carry on this time if only she didn't start to yell.
Then he'd have to put the brake on, for he
couldn't afford to let the people in the other flats
hear a girl yelling in his room. He didn't want
to have a cloud of witnesses to the thing he
wanted to do. But he didn't think there was
any real risk of a yell to-night. Even though
she did yell the last time there were signs that
she was beginning to get into her stride. She
came, if she came at all, expecting things to
happen, and she had no reason to grumble if she
wasn't disappointed. Besides there was the
present he had bought for her nestling up on the

59

mantelshelf in its satin-lined casket; a twenty-guinea gold and jewelled wristlet watch which was worth something more than a kiss. A big expense, he thought, but she was worth it. . . . Oh, she was fairer than the evening air clad in the beauty of a thousand stars. . . . Not quite so wonderful as that, but she was fair, and he was mad for her.

Everything was ready, and everything was waiting for her. The room was aglow with the heat from a blazing fire. Everything whispered encouragement to, and tolerance of, the solace of sex enjoyment. Food, fruit, and flowers; light glowing softly through amber shades; the bottle of wine offering exhilaration; cushions coyly clamouring for the vivid conclusion of passion. And all would contribute to, and form a happy harmony, hiding in softness and colour the savageness and sadness born in the energy and ecstasy of the sex encounter.

After they had taken supper they could sit down courageously and cosily on the divan. He wouldn't force or even press her to take any wine, but if she would take a glass or two, all the better. After a little while he would place the watch around her wrist . . . and listen to her cries of admiration . . . he would kiss and kiss her while he was looking quietly to see how her

things were fastened . . . then fondle some of
them open here and there . . . so that when the
right moment paused in front of him, a little
struggle, sweet and rapid, would be a sweet
beginning of a sweeter end.

He glanced around the room to see that
everything was in order. To see that there was
nothing that would even delicately interfere with
the plans or the excited emotions of the evening.
There now; look at it, look at it, look at it! He
had overlooked the print of Lochner's picture
of the Crucifixion, hanging on the wall so that
when she was lying on the divan, it would be
staring her in the face . . . that gruesome,
beautiful, tranquil, primitive expression of the
last terrible act of the Passion. . . . To the right
on the Cross the stark, wasted figure of Jesus
with the look of predestined, agonizing resigna-
tion on His tortured, peaceful face. . . . Three
wondering, funny-looking angels, fluttering like
little birds in the air, each with a tiny chalice in
tiny hands; two of them catching in the tiny
cups the blood that trickled from the nail-
wounds in His hands; the third gathering in the
cup the blood that streamed from His wounded
side. . . . Mary Magdalene, dressed in brown
and modified purple, kneeling at the foot of the
Cross, the train of her gown sweeping around a

bare skull and a bare bone. . . . To the left of the picture, the rich purple-mantled St. John supporting the fainting, black-gowned figure of the Saviour's Mother. . . . Behind, the peaceful features of a valley, with a narrow, curving, swift-flowing brook in its bosom. . . . And high up in the background, to the left, on a tiny indication of a road, the little figure of a soldier marching up and down on guard.

That picture would have to come down and be hidden away for a while. It was bound to be a disturbing element. Once let it catch her eye, and superstitious fear would make her briskly button up all her secrets, and fend her back into a condition of agitated and implacable primness. Besides he wouldn't feel perfectly comfortable himself, now since his attention had hovered around it. Something strange and sorrowful would be there contesting silently everything they said, everything they did. It must come down and be set aside. Perhaps that very picture was the influence that stood in the way on previous occasions when she was here, and was ready apparently to go the whole hog, and then suddenly became hard and denying. . . . Curious that it never occurred to him before. He extended his hand to take it from the wall, and withdrew it again. He wished

62

the picture had never been where it was. . . .
He felt a chill thrill at the thought of removing
it. Was he getting superstitious too? He
laughed softly and deridingly at the thought. . . .
It was pitiful that this silly feeling of nervous-
ness should dart through him. . . . He wasn't a
Catholic or even a Christian, so down, down you
come. He turned his head a little aside, and
pressing his lips together, he lifted the picture
from the wall, smiling, to rebuke his infirmity
of sudden fear, went into another room quietly
and deliberately, and placed the picture behind
a bookcase there. Returning he sat down,
lighted a cigarette, and puffed and puffed, and
waited tremulously. She was twenty minutes
behind her time now, and that wasn't promising.
She really was a provoking little bitch. Between eight-thirty and nine—that was what she
had written to him, and have a nice little supper
ready for his little darling. Well, the supper
was here, but where was the little darling? And
at the end of the letter that she wouldn't be later
than nine-fifteen, so if she wasn't with him by
nine-twenty, he needn't wait, for she wouldn't be
coming. . . . Nine-twenty now, and she wasn't
here. . . . One thing certain—if she didn't
come to-night, she had seen the last of him. He
toyed with the flowers in the vase on the table;

he read the label on the bottle of wine; he put
some more coal on the fire; he crossed to the
window, pulled the curtains aside and looked
out on to the street; he pulled the curtains back,
returned to his seat by the fire and smoked
furiously. . . . A quarter to ten, by God, and
she hadn't come. If she wasn't coming,
couldn't she 'phone, and not keep him waiting
this way for her? Or if she was afraid of re-
proaches if she 'phoned, couldn't she at least
send a telegram? He took a little book mech-
anically, opened it and began to read a few lines.
. . . "Critics have referred to Monet as being of
Norman birth, when as a fact his mother was of
a Lyons' family, and the artist was born in
Paris. . . ." Happy Paris, happy Monet. . . .
Lucky fellows these artists who could make a
high hill of dainty, fragrant garments stripped
from pretty women. . . . If he were a sculptor
or a painter or something of that kind, this jade
wouldn't be keeping him waiting like this, time
nipping into his anticipations of delight with
uncertainty and misgiving. . . . Still she might
come yet. . . . Many things in London might
delay her. . . . The traffic . . . a bad jam. . . .
Ticking of the clock getting on his nerves. . . .
He'd just wait patiently a little longer, then if
she didn't come he'd seek a compensation down

in Piccadilly. . . . Ten times the little clock on
the mantelpiece struck. . . . He sat like a stone
listening, puffed up with rage and disappointment. The clock stopped striking and resumed
its laughing tick, tick, tick. He sat there still
as a stone. . . . He saw his maid come in, leave
a small tray of things on the table beside him,
and heard her say "Cup of tea" while he was
"wyting" . . . "didn't look as if she'd come to-
night . . . wot a shime, and things so nice and
comfy. . . ." He sat there still as a stone, sick
and hot with rage and disappointment. . . . His
mind went forth savagely and sought her out;
his hands went round her throat and he shook
her and shook her. Perhaps it was just as well.
. . . What fools men were to lacerate their
senses with these delicious and dangerous
emotions. . . . He sipped his tea with a stiff,
set face, and nibbled his toast, while his hands
in imagination circled her throat and shook, and
shook and shook her. . . . He would go out
and take a long walk, a swift walk, a furious
walk, and sweat all his longing and disappointment out of him. . . . He put on his heavy coat
and wrapped a muffler round his neck. . . . His
eye fell on the little blue box on the mantelpiece,
and snapping it open he fixed the gold and
jewelled watch round his wrist. . . . She had

65

missed something, anyhow, by not coming to
him. . . . Then he descended the stairs and
passed out into the street. She could come
now if she liked. . . . Hoped she would. Price
of her to come and find him out. . . .

Here was a taxi coming up the street. . . . No,
but she might be in it. . . . He'd peep as it
passed. Damn fellows allowed to drive too
quickly. Couldn't snatch a glimpse of who-
ever was in it, he flashed past so fast. . . .
Dangerous speed altogether. He'd go back a
little just to see if it stopped at his place. . . .
Wouldn't go back though if she was in it. . . .
No demeaning himself that way. Damned taxi
had flown past his place. Might have known
it couldn't have been she.

He tightened again his loosened emotions,
and walked swiftly, never lowering the quick-
ness of his pace till he came into sight of a glow
in the near distance that told him he was coming
into the colour-lighted sprightliness of Piccadilly
Circus. Pausing at the corner by Swan and
Edgar's, he looked on at the streaming, hurrying, pleasure-seeking, prettily dressed, neatly
dressed, snappily dressed hordes that surged
along and around, that crossed and passed and
crossed again in all the curious, bewildering,
merging and rejecting jugglery of human life

and movement. The circle of life streamed
round and round, moving off the Circle down
Shaftesbury Avenue, towards Leicester Square,
or up Regent Street. Long, lithe limousines,
purring confidently, joining in the orgy of movement, slipped by with a majestic glide, passing
superciliously the perky little two-seaters that
raced vehemently alongside for awhile, then
shamedly dropped behind and followed afar off
with a cringe in their perkiness. Bull-bodied
taxis, graceless, assertive, self-absorbed, facing
forward, ignoring all the wheels around them,
nosing boldly up to the front of a traffic jam,
standing still or rushing along, ever determinedly
minding their own particular business. Buses,
big and red-faced, abrim with strength, bullying
their rumbling way through the traffic, trum-
peted around corners with engine-whirr and
horn-hoot. And all this streamed in, rushed
round, and poured out within a blazing halo of
lights, rich blue, light blue, purple, bright red,
pale red, rich green, light green, mauve, yellow,
and orange, flashing, dimming, vanishing,
moving slowly, whirling fast, rippling down
yellow, rippling up green, gliding across to the
left red, gliding purple across to the right,
making an endless flow and ebb of animated
colour. Over opposite, a steady, dignified,

silvery yellow glow told that a Cochran Revue had a home there. The name of an actress that carried a terrible load of loveliness about with her, blazed imperiously in golden lights on the breast of Shaftesbury Avenue. Over to the right, on a great broad space, a shower of red, yellow and green stars, flanked by zigzagging, curving lines of red and green, merged into a huge, gorgeously flamed announcement of an unction of beer in flashing yellow, changing in a moment to half green and half yellow; then all yellow, again with a crimson strip in the centre of each letter; then the upper half became red and the lower half remained yellow; then it was entirely red; then all green; then the upper half red and the lower half green, then it became all yellow again, to vanish in darkness and give place again in a few moments to the shower of red, yellow, and green stars that recommenced its cycle of announcement. On the wall of a restaurant in brilliant colours were an orange sunbright blue sea and emerald-green trees of some resort in Southern Europe. The whole place flamed with the gaudy gusto of advertisement.

But he hadn't come here to look at the lights, he hadn't come here to look at the lights. He came to get a woman. But the woman must be

something worth while to compensate him for
what he had missed. He hummed softly to
himself:

> I wanna woman, oh, bo, I wanna woman,
> With wavy hair and time to spare to banish care,
> I wanna woman, I wanna wanna woman,
> wanna woman.
> That's always gay, doesn't pray; for last hours o' night,
> first hours o' day;
> I wanna woman, I wanna woman.
> That'll say, oh gee, my guy, you know the way;
> now my clothes are astray, you know the way,
> my guy; oh gee,
> I wanna woman, I wanna wanna woman . . .
> to-day!

He watched a man coming towards him with
a placard hanging over his breast looped over
his shoulders to another hanging down his back.
He read the one in front, "The wages of Sin is
Death." He looked at the face of the man
passing and saw there a sign of severe, sodden,
and enviously imagined sanctity. He watched
him, moving quietly and obstinately onward,
mingling with the crowd, looking to neither the
right nor the left, carrying his holy placard
glorified with the reflected glow of the vanishing, reappearing, gleaming, twisting, rippling,
coloured lights of the Circus. Nobody took the
slightest notice of this wandering herald of

heaven. He wondered—oh that wasn't a bad little bird that passed; face just a little bit too coarse though—at the curious sensations different people sought to bring them pleasure. Churches were old-fashioned. Hanging on still to pulpits and placards. No novelty in them now; what was wanted were Stations of the Cross in coloured electric lights.   Ireland's one-up there, for, in Dublin, he remembered seeing a statue of the Blessed Virgin with a ring of coloured electric bulbs around her head for a halo. Unbecoming thoughts for a man on a mission like his, so he crossed the Circus and wandered down Piccadilly towards Leicester Square, humming softly to himself:

> I wanna woman, I wanna woman,
> For first hours o' day, last hours o' night,
> I wanna, wanna, wanna woman.

He kept watching out keenly for a suitable bit of skirt. They were streaming past him, many giving him an enquiring and desirous glance as they went by. No, thank you, he wouldn't have any of those. They were all so common, so coarse, and so obvious. He wanted just a little elegance of manner and a saucy reticence that surrendered with a sad, sham charm what it was paid for and had to give. These were rare among birds, for their life muddied their manners as well as their bodies.

He passed into a bright patch of coloured light on the pavement flowing from a window display of green, black, crimson, and yellow dresses. Glancing casually at the richer light and colour in the window, he saw a woman leaving it and walking off in the opposite direction. Pretty, dressed in a smartly-made tailored suit, covered by a fur coat that reached to the hem of the skirt, short enough to show the full knee when she took a step forward; a delicious helmet hat of modest red made a sweet frame for her face. His indifference flaming into excited interest, he swung round, said "Sorry" to a man he bumped into, and hurriedly walked after her. Was she one? Hard to say. She seemed to have an elegance and taste in dress, and a gracefulness in walk that few tarts had, but there still seemed to be something about her that suggested the possibility of hire. He'd walk on quickly, get in front of her, stop at a shop-window and eye her as she passed. He went by her rapidly, walked on in front for a few moments, stopped at a shop-window, watching her sideways as she came along. His heart beat a little faster as he saw first the right, then the left leg from the knee down issuing out of the narrow sweep of

71   F

her neatly tailored frock.   Trim, and he loved
them trim, and with this bird everything else
seemed to be in coy conformity with the pretty
legs.   He wheeled around as she came level
with him, and looked longingly and enquiringly
at her, but she apparently took no notice and
walked on.   This was disappointing, and made
things doubtful.   Was she one, or was she not?
She was worth following for a while, and if she
only would turn down one of the quieter streets,
he'd tighten up to her, and ask her how she felt
towards the world.   Wouldn't be nice to get a
choke-off in a crowd, so he'd wait a quieter chance
to find out if her clothes came off easily.   He
hadn't the courage yet to go up and say "Good
evening" and chance it.   She might be waiting
for some man to do the clicking quietly.   Some
birds were like that—only out occasionally to
add a little week-end tail to their wages; or,
those that were a little new at the game, and still
frightened and shy.   If he wasn't quick some
johnny was bound to nip in and she'd be
snapped up before his eyes just because he
hadn't enough of the pure stuff in him to
Charleston up to her and whisper, "Say, kid,
you'd look nicer with a little less on; oh, you'd
look a lot nicer with a lot less on. . . ."   Damn
this leisurely moving crowd that was hindering

his efforts to keep close to her. He could see
in the distance the little, soft red hat dodging
forward, in and out through the people,
apparently with ease and certainty, while every
man and every woman that came toward him
seemed to plonk themselves right in front of his
face, and then begin to dodge the wrong way
to get by. He hurried and twisted as cleverly
as he could. She was a lovely bird, and he'd
willingly bury four or even five quid under the
world-forgetting trickeries of a night with her.
There was the soft little red hat crossing
Wardour Street. He'd hurry, reach her, walk
side by side and get it over before his halting
hesitation lost her. . . .

Now he was caught in a crowd gathered at the
edge of the path gaping greedily at something
that probably wasn't worth a flickering thought,
coming up Wardour Street . . . Oh, procession of
people singing something like a hymn. . . .
Church Parade. Leader carrying a cross. . . .
Lift the cross higher, brother. . . . Choir in white
surplices and black cassocks with heads rever-
ently bent over their hymn-books. Jammed here
now for at least three minutes and the soft little
red hat getting farther and farther away. . . . Why
do the authorities shut their eyes to this sort of
wandering, maundering, philandering missionary

mania holding up regular and necessary traffic? My God, listen to them.

Lord in this Thy Mercy's day, ere it pass for aye away
On our knees we fall and pray.

No use, gentlemen; no one in Piccadilly has the slightest intention of falling on his knees. . . . She'd be miles away before he'd get himself out of this mess. . . . Hurry up, hurry up; get along, please. . . .

Holy Jesus grant us tears, fill us with heart-searching
     fears
Ere that awful doom appears.

Soft, sloppy, winding, creeping, crawling, snaily, snobby, snaring bastards dividing him from all the heart-quickening gifts beneath the red hat, the tailored suit, and the silk stockings. . . . Oh, if he were a savage how he'd like to jump in and spear a hundred per cent of them. . . . Not a sign of her now. That procession had crossed the hunt and saved the quarry. He breathed deeply in disappointment and rancour. And they did this sort of thing out of their love for men. Annoying thing to come up against and mingle with his present mood. Even if he did manage to get into touch with her again, things wouldn't feel so comfortable, for he knew the hymn by heart, and here it was maliciously humming in his mind,

blunting the innocence of his eagerness. She
might be anywhere now. . . . Grant us tears . . .
fill us with heart-searching fears. . . . No use of
looking any longer. . . . To go home is best. . . .
Nothing in skirts could interest him now till he'd
forgotten a little about the girl in the soft red hat.
A peach. . . . No doubt about it, he'd missed a
peach. . . . Lord in this Thy mercy's day, ere it
pass for aye away. . . . Bakerloo, from Piccadilly
to Baker Street, and then a bus to Swiss Cottage.
. . . On our knees we fall and pray. . . . It was
just twelve anyhow, and only the "Pros" that
time has tossed a lot paraded now. . . . Strange,
determinedly sliding movement of the esca-
lators. . . . Wonder how the procession would
look coming up or going down one of them. . . .
Keep time and step off together, please. . . .
Trains going west . . . that was his platform . . .
empty carriage . . . drowse to Baker Street. . . .
When eyes are closed curious feeling runs
through body with the gentle rumbling shake in
the movement of a tube train. . . . Feeling of
motion and of rest . . . Oxford Circus. . . . Two
more stations. . . . Somebody coming in . . .
sitting opposite him. . . . Woman . . . see so by
shoes. Some uninteresting looking old cow or
young heifer not worth noticing. . . . Keep his
eyes closed . . . Regent's Park. . . . Next stop. . . .

Nothing exciting in the night after all his hope.
. . . Procession spoilt everything. . . . Procession
spoilt sport. . . . Perhaps it was just as well to get
a check now and again. Thoughtless compli-
ance with the complaints of sex was bound to over-
balance his nervous system, and that wouldn't do
at all. He was almost glad now that the procession had poked its way between him and his
desire to make a fool of himself. He wouldn't
feel that seething sense of remorse that invariably
followed a night with a new woman; the dead,
revolting dissatisfaction of deliriously misspent
energy and passion; the miserable surge of empti-
ness that followed the feat of giving too much for
a short enjoyment. He could rest and go to sleep
without the soul-nagging sense of sex weariness.
Perhaps this would be the first step towards a
stronger self-directed life, of decided and per-
sistent effort towards self-control. Back to a
virtuous bed. . . . Good bed; better bed; best bed.

Baker Street . . . oh hell, don't stir. . . . Fur
coat, tailored suit, and soft red hat sitting
opposite. Damn fool keep eyes closed. Where's
she getting. . . . Passing Marylebone. Oh, that
was a cute glance. . . . Measuring up his naughti-
ness. Opening her fur coat. Too hot in here,
dearie. Good sign; wants to show her legs. . . .
Passing Warwick Avenue. . . . She's a peach,

boys, she's a peach. . . . A sense of uncomfortable
fulness made his heart beat faster. . . . He lighted
a cigarette, and his hand shook. . . . His nerves
were tingling again. . . . Oh, gee, my guy, you
know the way, now my clothes are astray, you
know the way, my guy, oh gee, you wanna wanna
wanna woman. . . . Getting out at Maida Vale. . . .
So was he, you bet. . . . Along the passages to the
lift. . . . He feverishly paid his excess fare from
Baker Street to Maida Vale to the attendant,
watching her from the other end of the lift. Anyhow, she knew that he was interested in her.
She had seen him look at her with suggestion in
his eyes, and had shown no annoyance. Indeed,
she had sent him glances that seemed to venture
an invitation. The lift doggedly moved up-
wards, came to the road-level, the gates crashed
open, and they passed out into the street. If
she hopped off quickly now, all was over, but if
she went on slowly the thing promised fruit.
The street was quiet and restful, animated only
by an odd taxi cruising past. Up in the sky, in
the north-west shone The Plough and in the
north-east sparkled The Lyra. . . . She went along
slowly. His mouth that had dried twitched a
little, and his heart beat unpleasantly as he
hurried on and walked by her side. . . . "Good
evening," he murmured nervously. She gave a

slow, careless glance at him, and continued to walk on slowly. . . . "The air is very clear to-night," he went on, "and the stars are remarkably plain. . . ."

She turned her head to him, smiled and said, "What are you doing with yourself at this time of night?"

He stammered a little as he murmured, "Oh, just taking a stroll round about thoughtlessly."

"You passed me in Piccadilly," she asked, "didn't you?"

"Yes," he said, "I think that I did see you somewhere in Piccadilly."

She's very cool about it all, he thought; she must be a bird after all.

"Well, now that you've seen me again," she said, "do you fancy me as much as ever?"

She was a Pro then, so he'd have to be carefully indifferent, for the more desire he showed, the higher would be the fee.   So he kept silent.

"You'd like to come up to my flat and have a drink or a cup of tea, wouldn't you?" she asked.

"Yes, I wouldn't mind," he answered.

"I'm afraid if I let you come you might want to be naughty, would you, my dear?" she asked smilingly.

"I might, you never know," he answered.

"If I let you come, and was very nice to you, you'd give me a little present, darling?"

"Oh, of course," he replied.

"How much?"

"Two pounds," he murmured.

"You're not out to spend much!" she said disdainfully, hastening away from him. "Cheerio, darling!"

He hurried after her and said, "Don't run away, dear; let's talk together for a minute or two. There's no necessity to rush off in a rage."

"I'm not in a rage, dear," she said, "but I don't let myself be man-mauled for two quid. Go back to Piccadilly and you'll get lots of girls ready to accommodate themselves to your idea of generosity."

He was fascinated; she was a rare bird, and he didn't want to lose her, but he wanted to get his pleasure as cheaply as possible.

"How much do you want then, to let me go home and make a fuss of you?" he asked.

"Five pounds, at least," she said.

"That's a lot of money for a few hours. I'll give you four," he bargained.

"Five, dear, or there's nothing doing. If you fancied me so much, and followed me so long, I'm worth a fiver."

He walked beside her pondering, fingering in

his pocket one note from another and counting thoughtfully. . . . One . . . two . . . three . . . four . . . five . . . six . . . seven . . . and a ten-bob note.

"Oh, be a sport," she said encouragingly, "and I'll give you a right good time."

"All right," he answered, "I'll give the fiver."

Stopping at a house of flats, she took a key from her bag, opened the hall door, ascended to the first floor, where she rang a bell; the door of the flat was opened by a maid who gave him a quick, furtive look as they entered. She brought him into a sitting-room, quietly and comfortably furnished with easy-chairs and lounges. Some ordinary landscapes were on the walls, and on the mantelpiece were two large photographs of pretty women pictured in a state of saucy and semi-nudity. She pulled brilliantly green curtains that were on the window closer together, as she said to him: "Take off your coat, dear, and make yourself at home."

To the right of the fireplace were six shelves filled with books. Spicy, naughty, and non-sensical, the lot of them, he thought.

"Tilly," she called to the maid, "bring me and my gentleman friend some tea and biscuits."

She took off her fur coat and soft red hat, and sat down in one of the easy-chairs before the fire,

crossing one leg over the other. "Nice to be
sitting before a fire on a cold night like this," she
said as she sipped her tea.

"Nothing better," he said, "with a pretty girl
waiting to be nice to you."

"And with a man that wants to be naughty,"
she added.

"I see," he said, "you're interested in books."

"Just a little," she answered, glancing at the
shelves. "They pass in a pleasant way many a
dull hour."

"Who's your favourite writer?" he asked.

"I've none," she said. "I like Hardy, France,
and Dostoievsky a lot."

"Dostoievsky's one of the Russian fellows,"
he said; "don't know how anyone could be
interested in such a writer, though I haven't read
him myself."

"If you haven't, how do you know?" she asked.

"I know from those that tried to read him," he
said, "that he's a terrible writer."

"Yes," she admitted, "he is, sometimes . . .
terrible."

"Who's the johnny that wrote all the books
you have covered in green?"

"Balzac," she said. "Wonderful writer.
Never read his *Poor Relations*? *Madame Marneffe*,
Baron Hulot, and *Cousin Pons*—far greater than

his better known *Old Goriot*. Powerful realism,
and pathetic, remorseless imagination."

"Come over here," he said, "and sit beside
me; I don't want to be bothered about Balzac
just now."

She got up out of the chair, smiled, lifted her
skirt a little, danced over to him, and sat down by
his side on the settee. She put an arm round
his neck, kissed him quick and cooeed into his
face, the suggestive look in her eyes hardening a
little.

"Now, darling," she whispered, "what about
my little present? Not nice to talk about it, but
it's best to get all the nasty things over at once."

"Oh, I'll give it to you all right," he said.

"I know, but I might as well have it now."

"You won't trust me?" he asked peevishly.

"I know you're a sport," she said, "but it's just
as well to get it over and done with before we
begin to amuse ourselves."

He took the notes from his pocket with a
serious, half-timid sigh, and handed her five,
saying, "Here you are, five of the best and
brightest."

She quickly and gently caught hold of his
hand, and with a confident smile said, "The
ten-bob note as a little present for the maid,
dear."

"Oh, now you've had enough out of me," he protested.

"I always get a present for the maid," she insisted; "she's a dear woman, and I never forget to ask for a little tip for her. . . . Go on, don't spoil things now by a mean refusal of such a small thing; we're getting on so nicely together."

And the ten-shilling note was pulled gently from his hand, added to the five, and all were locked away in a drawer of a cabinet that stood quietly and expectantly close to the window. Then she removed her skirt, coat, and blouse, pulled loose the ribbons threading the shoulders of her cami-nickers, showing her breasts, animatedly sat beside him, put her arm round him, and murmured, "Now, darling, don't you like me a lot better with a little less on?"

He abandoned himself to the surge of desire that swept through him. He caught her in his arms and tried to bend her back on the settee. With a sour laugh she freed herself, crossed the room, and opened a door opposite.

"Come into the bedroom, dear," she said, "where we'll have plenty of room."

*   *   *

What a fool he had been to stop so long with her. It was maddening to have to stay on here

in bed beside her, after having got all that he
wanted. She had fallen asleep, while he was
still awake listening to the ticking of the little
clock at the other end of the room, thinking and
cursing deeply in his mind about the weariness
and waste of affection, energy, and money that
made this honeycomb a bitterness and a loathing
to him. He sat up in bed and winked his eyes
several times to press the heaviness out of them.
The first glimpse of a cold dawn was trickling in through the green curtains that covered
the window. The room that had looked too
full of nimbly dancing promises of pleasure
was now filled with a sickly sense of weariness,
and seemed to be stuffy with the breath of dead
things. He moved as far away as possible from
his companion, and looked down at her sleeping
there with her bare breasts, tossed hair and
partly open mouth. Attractiveness had ceased
to meddle with her now. He felt a wish to beat
till he bruised the breasts that he had fiercely
fondled only a few hours ago. Tear and rend
them for the ruin of tiredness and silent agony
of remorse that they had helped to bring upon
him. Lying here for three hours he had been
trying to deafen himself to his thoughts, and
put away the memories that had stormed his
mind before he had bargained with this un-

ashamed whore that now lay asleep and naked beside him. . . . The procession that had cut across his path and the hymn they had been singing. . . . "Holy Jesus, grant us tears, fill us with heart-searching fears. . . ." Keep it out, keep it out. . . . I wanna woman, I wanna woman, with wavy hair, to banish care, I wanna woman . . . keep it out, keep it out. . . .

She had felt him moving and was murmuring drowsily, "Lie down, sweetie; cold coming in under clothes, and I've nothing on . . . lie down, sweetie."

He plunged down into the bed again, and roughly pushed away a leg of hers that had wandered over near him. "Not so rough, dear," she murmured.

What vice-armoured souls these women had. But perhaps it was better if one wanted to be anything, to be that thing right out. Wallowing grandly in her own shame. Let the light of dawn but mount a little higher up and he'd slide from bed, and dress and leave this place of poisoned satisfaction.

Her eyes opened a little and a peculiar, spiteful smile darkened them, and her hand began to fondle him. "Keep that damned hand quiet," he said, as he jerked it away with a savage and resentful movement.

"Sweetie doesn't want pretty Alice any more," she murmured, giving his cheek a malicious caress.

"I'm going out of this," he said surlily, getting out of bed, and beginning to creep shiveringly into his clothes. Glancing in the glass he saw himself hollow-eyed, hair-tossed, with his chin darkened where his beard was beginning to show strongly.

She sat up sleepily, resting on her elbow, took a card from a drawer in a bedside table, held it out to him and said, "Card, dear, double ten double nine Berkeley. You might like to ring me up some evening."

Paying no attention to her, he tugged on his heavy coat, pulled on his hat, wrapped his muffler round his neck, glanced at the cabinet where his five pounds ten were stored, and said, "I'm off now, good-bye."

She snuggled down in the bed, pulled the clothes warmly round her shoulders and under her chin, and murmured, "Don't make a noise, dear, to wake the maid . . . she's such a dear woman, and I'm very fond of her . . . close the street door after you as gently as you can. . . . Cheerio, darling."

It was cold and damp coming into the air of the street. Leaving that whore warmly nested

86

in her bed, too. He was done with women for a long time. He kept his head bent as he slouched sleepily homewards. The exhaustion of the night was letting this dampness into his marrow. Ding, dong, ding, dong, dell. . . . Some damn church bell ringing for some damn service. Waste of time. . . . Never keep people from making fools of themselves. . . . Ding, dong, dell, sinners sent to hell, to clothe their pain in an everlasting yell; so cease to do evil, learn to do well; ding, dong, ding, dong, ding, dong, dell. . . . Palpitating nonsense, these bells.

He opened the door of his flat, and let himself shivering in. He would sleep till about five in the evening, then he would have a warm bath, a brandy and soda, a good dinner, and he would feel a lot better. He stripped to his shirt, and let his clothes slide from him in a heap on the floor. He slipped his pyjamas on over his shirt. Must be getting on for eight, now. . . . He bent his arm to look at his wrist. . . . Jesus, he had left the wristlet watch in the house of the whore! He didn't—he couldn't—have stuck it in one of his pockets. . . . He rummaged fiercely in the pockets of his trousers. . . . No, and he flung them savagely back on the floor. . . . His coat? He rummaged through the pockets of the coat . . . no, and flung it down again on the floor. . . . He remembered . . .

he had put it down on the little table beside the
bed, and had forgotten it was there in his eagerness to get away from the place. . . . Oh, the
idiot, the fool, the ape, to forget to take it up and
put it on when he was leaving. Oh, what a
stinkingly stupid thing to do. . . . What did he
want to bring it out with him for? And he had
no idea of the street or the house, only that they
were somewhere in Maida Vale. . . . He had
hurried away noticing nothing. . . . Wouldn't
take her card even. . . . Hadn't the least idea of
her telephone number. . . . A big-brained idiot,
that's what he was. . . . She had been well paid
for her favours—five pounds ten and a wristlet
watch and bangle worth twenty guineas. . . . She
was laughing at him now . . . and fitting it on. . . .
Pity it couldn't turn to steel and stop the circula-
tion of her blood. . . . He turned down the clothes
and stormed into bed. As he lay down his eye
caught sight of Lochner's Crucifixion hanging
again on the wall over his bed. . . . That blasted
maid of his couldn't keep from ferreting around.
. . . . Fished it out from behind the bookcase and
replaced it on the wall. . . . Frantic to meddle
with everything. . . . Mocking him there with its
tale of tragedy. . . . Take him weeks now to
recover from the shock of his stupidity. He
pressed himself down on the bed in a rush of rage.

I WANNA WOMAN

His head throbbed with the nerve-rack of his loss. Forget it and sleep. . . . That's all he could do . . . sleep and forget it. . . . He lay silent. . . . The telephone bell rang, rang . . . rang. He snapped down the receiver and bellowed "Hello? yes, this is Mr. Avreen. . . . Yes, it's Jack. . . . No, you can't come to-night. . . . I'll be engaged till long after midnight. . . . If you long to see me, why didn't you come last night? Explain . . . yes it will need some explanation . . . Angry? why of course I'm angry. No, I won't post the watch to you, or see you to-night either. . . . Must go now to keep an appointment." And he firmly and angrily replaced the receiver. . . . Then he gathered the clothes tightly around him, closed his eyes, and quivered in a mad medley of thoughts. This was the crowning of his foolishness. He stiffened with repressed and remorseful rage. . . . The telephone bell rang . . . and rang . . . and rang. . . . Ringing me again, he thought; well, let her ring.

A faint trickling beam of light from a timid rising sun crept in through the window and spread over the picture of the Crucifixion, showing wanly to the right the figure of Christ hanging on the Cross, the three funny little black-robed angels with tiny chalices in tiny hands catching the blood that dripped from hands and side;

Mary Magdalene, in her brown and purple robes, kneeling at the foot of the Cross; to the left the crimson-mantled St. John supporting the fainting Mother; the brook swiftly flowing through the peaceful valley, and away in the dim distance, the little figure of a careless soldier marching up and down on guard.

And he tightened his teeth together, cursed deeply and lay still, as the telephone bell rang . . . rang . . . rang.

THE STAR-JAZZER

THE stars glittered in the sky and the frost glittered on the ground as she bent her head and watched the water flowing slowly into the bucket. It was a blasted shame that they didn't get a pipe to give a quicker flow for the poor people. It was terrible when the ten families that lived in the house were looking for water at the same time. And when the people that lived in the houses on each side were at their own pipes, this one dwindled down to a tiny, maddening dribble of drops. She often ground her teeth when she came into the yard for a bucketful to find before her one washing a cabbage under a flow of water, another waiting her turn with a basin of spuds, and a third humming a tune, with a kettle to be filled. The best plan was to fill a pail overnight, so as to be certain that nothing would delay her husband from his hasty wash and hurried breakfast before he sallied out to work.

That was the bell of St. George's chiming
twelve o'clock, pushing another Tuesday up
against the pile of Tuesdays that she had put
behind her. Tuesday . . . the day she hated,
the day she dreaded, the day she felt was always
in front of her. The day that, when she thrust
it behind her, seemed with a rapid, wheeling
circle to stand before her again. The day that,
when through the week she had dried the
clothes, ironed and aired them, came up, shook
her from bed at six o'clock to restart the washing of them and kept her going sullenly, cease-
lessly, and silently, with pain and without pity,
till twelve o'clock at night, carrying up clean
water, washing, wringing, rinsing, washing,
wringing, and rinsing and wringing, and carrying down ten flights of stairs the water soiled
with the mud of clothes after a week of wearing.
For eight years now, every Tuesday, on the
stairs coming down, on the stairs going up, or
standing in the yard as she was now, except when
she was having a kid, she had listened to the bell
of St. George's chiming the twelve strokes that
divided one day from another.

She shivered, glanced up at the sky, and
wondered what they called the star that glittered
right over her head. It seemed to stand out in
the black breast of the sky in a fuller and more

friendly way than the others; you could say
the others shone, but this one gleamed. Her
mother had often told her when she was a kid
that God was hiding behind the stars; that they
were resting-places for the angels' feet when
they were flying from one part of the heavens
to the other; and that at midnight on Christmas
Eve all the stars danced. She wondered would
it be a schottische or a waltz they danced. She
had never yet met anybody that saw them dancing. Like many another yarn, she supposed it
was all a fake. Though anything could have
happened on the first midnight eve of the first
Christmas. She could picture the Infant lying
in the manger motionless, or stretching out His
arm towards His Mother, with St. Joseph standing stiff behind her, and the shepherds in one
corner, and the kings in the other, staring open-
mouthed at the now delicate, now delirious dance
of the stars in the heavens. . . . Wouldn't it be
funny now if they started to do a jazz dance
across the sky? She'd pick the movement up,
and join them with a rush. "Chase me, Charlie,
through the clouds and over the sky-i-i!" Not
to-night though, after a day of washing the
clothes of Jack and herself and the kids that
were dirtied through the week's wear in the
streets and in the tenement. An elegant sight

she'd look with her legs all soppy wet from the thighs down, stiff and tightened up with the work she'd done, doing a Jazz or a Charleston round a star. Step, step, together, dip; step, step, together, dip. Dipping, maybe, when she should be bringing her feet together; and stepping when she should be doing a dip. She'd have to postpone it to a happier day; but give her a month's rest from the husband and kids, a few pounds for a new little frock, and she'd do a Jazz or a Charleston in the full, flooding light of the biggest star in the firmament. . . . How do you do do dodoodle loodo do dooo. . . . Kick them up and kick them high; show a knee and show a thigh, don't be shy, to the stars shining bright in the sky . . . in the sky. . . . She felt a surge moving through her body. A desire to circle around the lonely yard, surrounded by the surly-featured tenements, now dark and still, sheltering the sleeping, to sing softly, to move and wag her body through the rhythms of a Charleston or a Jazz; to show the star that, in spite of seven kids carried in ten years, her figure was still shapely; that her hair was still long and thick, and the gold gleams in the brown weren't all gone; that her face, hiding its lines in the darkness, had all its beauty left. She bent back her head and stared up at the star. Then she

began to move her body to the tune and motions
of a Jazz, circling round the yard while the water
poured lazily from the pipe, filled the pail, and
flowed over the rim, down the sides, and disappeared into the gully beneath. She stepped
forward with her left foot, then with her right,
brought her feet together and dipped by bending her legs backward from the knees. She
moved forward, twisted, turned and came back
again. Step, step, step, together, dip, with her
head bent back, gazing at the star. As she
moved she felt her wet skirt sopping, sopping
against her knees, so as she moved on, step, step,
she unloosened her skirt at the waist, together,
dip; and as she rose to step forward again, the
skirt fell from her, and she danced on in her
short black petticoat. With her hair flowing down, in her untidily buttoned blouse,
dingy black petticoat, patched shoes, and imita-
tion silk stockings, ribbed and scarred with
many a mended ladder, round the tenement-
enclosed yard she turned, bent, circled, advanced,
retreated, across and around the yard, singing
with her head bent back, staring at the star—

Now a woman, and once a kid
That came from God—oh yes, I dih-i-d;
I came from God, and I settled down
In this damn'd and dreary one-horse tow-ow-n;

THE STAR-JAZZER

I came from God and I settled down
In this damn'd and dreary one-horse town!

I met a man and lost my head,
Oh yes, I did, I lost my he-he-head;
And him I wed; he gives me bread,
And fits my life into a four-post beh-e-ed;
And him I wed; he gives me bread,
And fits my life into a four-post bed!

I'll sing and dance beneath the sky,
Out of my cage, with no one ni-i-igh;
Not caring why—make joy a rage,
The clouds a hall and that bright star a sta-a-age.
Not caring why—make joy a rage,
The clouds a hall, and that bright star a stage!

She was getting excited. She danced down the yard, dipping, rising, and stepping more rapidly than before. Now a woman—and her eyes gleamed grandly—once a kid that came from God . . . oh yes—her breath was coming in quick, impulsive pants—she did. She came from God, and she settled down in this damned town and—she whirled to the right and hurried forward—dreary one-horse town. She met a man and lost her head, oh yes, she did, she met a man and lost her . . . step, step, together, dip, and him she wed; he gives her bread, and fits her life into a four-post bed. . . . She swung her arms wildly as she plunged along, dipping, stepping,

96

and bringing her feet together, dipping again
and moving forward, going round and round
the yard furiously, heatedly, wagging her behind, swaying her body madly, sweat beading
her forehead and trickling down her cheeks. . . .
She was tiring, her legs were aching vividly; her
heart beat and beat so rapidly that she was almost unable to breathe. . . . She staggered on,
bending stiffly and clumsily now, losing her balance frequently so that she almost fell several
times. . . . She stiffened her muscles determinedly and, struggling on, danced out the wild,
reckless, happy-mad rhythm of the song she
sang, with savage, panting breath, with movement of leg, sway of body, and stamp of foot,
with her head bent back, and her eyes staring
up at the star. . . . Out of my cage, with no one
ni-i-igh, not caring why—make joy a rage, the
clouds a hall and that bright star a st-a-age. . . .
She began to sag at the knees. A sharp pain
was shooting through her legs. . . . The small of
her back was a dull, gnawing ache. She lifted
her feet in a dull, heavy way from the ground as
she swayed along. The star was moving from
side to side and up and down as she stared at it.
She felt all the vim was going, going out of her;
the chant became a murmur, a fading murmur
slipping lifelessly from the feverish breath-pants.

97

Then suddenly in the centre of the yard she sank down on her knees, and leaned heavily and wearily against the wooden upright that held the pipe from which the water still lazily flowed, filling the pail, trickling down the sides, and disappearing down the gully underneath. . . . There she lay lingering in a glow of weariness, head bent, shoulder leaning against the wooden upright, and her body cooped up in a kneeling curl in the centre of the paved yard, the tall, lounging, filth-fostered whores of houses all around her. . . . She held her right hand out and let the water from the pipe flow over it, making a tiny cascade as it fell over into the pail, and she listened curiously to the gentle gurgle of the overflow as it slid down into the gully beneath. . . . One of her kids gurgled something like that a moment before it went west.   Where was it now?   Up, up, up, somewhere, dodging about in heaven, behind the bloody star, maybe.   Blast the star and damn the star, anyway.   I want to look at it no more, never again.   Let it rot, rot, rot in the sky. . . . No, no, she mustn't curse a star; dangerous thing to do. . . . No one could tell how close a star could be to God. . . . Badges of the blessed angels maybe. . . . Silly thing to do, but she was always doing silly things. . . . Rings on the finger of God, maybe. . . . Wish she could get hold of one to pawn. . . . Imagine her going into Lowry's with a star in a basket. Taking it out, planting it down on the counter, and asking Sammy how much he would give on that. Oh, she must try to keep these desecrational thoughts from creeping into her mind.

*   *   *

She slowly and unwillingly gathered herself together, and pulled and pulled herself up on to her feet. She turned the tap and stopped the water flowing from the pipe. She tilted the pail and spilled some of the water out, bent and lifted up the skirt that had fallen from her in the dance, and flung it over her shoulder, took up the pail in her right hand, walked unsteadily across the yard, lifted the latch of the yard door, and passed into the darkness of the back hall of the house. She groped her way along the darkness, her fingers brushing the wall, her lungs, after the coolness and freshness of the outside air, sensing the hot, human, thicker density of the air in the house that gave breath and took breath from the forty-five breathing bodies that lived there. Her hand touched the foot of the banisters, and gripping the handrail she began to go up the stairs. With the pull of the pail intensifying an ache in the muscles of her right arm, and the pull of the

99

handrail intensifying an ache in the muscles of her
left arm, she climbed the first flight, crossed the
little landing, climbed the second flight, crossed
the lobby and went on. . . . Her foot slipped on
something soft and slimy on the stairs; dirty gang
of mellowing apes; some kid misbehaved on the
stairs, and nobody bothered to clean it away.
She climbed on heavily to the fourth floor of the
tenement. . . . Here she left her pail on the floor,
and paused and panted. . . . She felt very unsteady; her legs were hot and quivering with a
curious tremble. What a fool she had been to
do that dance. . . . Two more flights of damned
stairs to climb before she got to where the bed
harboured a hope of sleep. . . . No, there wouldn't
be much sleep to-night with those aching muscles
and trembling legs. . . . Eight flights done, and
two more before her still. Ten altogether.
She must have climbed these twenty times to-day.
That was two hundred flights climbed carrying
water, and two hundred flights done downwards,
without counting the washing, the wringing, and
the cooking. Well, God could see her job
wasn't a soft one, anyway. All done to keep life
pure and wholesome. Well, the majesty of God
gilds the homes of the poor. She offered the
burden and the pain of the day to Jesus. She
forgot the dance; she couldn't offer that. It

would be blasphemy or something like that. The
dance had taken the good out of the offering
of her day's hard labour. She must have gone
out of her mind for a few moments. She felt
curious. As if there were things near that were
about to touch her. . . . A shivering tremble that
tingled her skin passed slowly over her whole
body. She was frightened. . . . She shouldn't
think of speaking about God in this dark landing
at this time of night. . . . She always felt shuddery
whenever she thought of sacred things in the
dark. . . . She looked backwards down the stairs
and saw a large bright star shining in through
the window of the lobby below. She could sense
a cold mockery in its gleam. She never felt the
place so quiet before. Everybody must be fast
asleep. . . . Yet she felt that there were things
very near her, breathing on her, stretching out
hands to touch her. Again she felt the tingling
shiver, cold and creepy, passing up her legs,
through her body, right up and over the skin of
her head. She stopped quickly, caught up the
pail, and ran swiftly up the other two flights of
stairs, pushed the door of her room open, stepped
inside and closed it rapidly and fearfully behind
her, standing against it trembling and thankful
to be hemmed in from fear of the darkness and
silence by the satisfying reality of her one-

roomed home. There were the strings stretching from wall to wall that carried the washing; the three chairs, side by side, around the fire, hidden by the damper clothes steaming steadily into a drier condition. The kitchen table, pushed back against the wall, with an oil-lamp on it that was giving a smoky light to the room: the large rosy-featured wall-paper that did its best to look cheery and contented; the huge bed that gave a grudging rest to them all, with her three eldest asleep at the foot, her husband lying on his back at the head, with the youngest lying on his right side.

Placing the pail in a corner, she went to the fire and, stripping one of the chairs of the steaming clothes, she turned it around and sat down wearily upon it. Lifting her petticoat she warmed her legs. She was frozen, and she felt a little sick. Near one o'clock now, it must be, and she had to be up at six in the morning. Five hours of sleep was hardly enough for a young woman that had to work so hard. Hoped the kids at the bottom of the bed would sleep to-night without their usual kicking and squirming and plunging about. Hoped to God they would. Six kids in eight years. Her belly must have been working like a steam-engine; cranks twisting, piston rods shooting out and shooting in;

wheels revolving . . . chih, chih . . . chih chih chih, without a stop, going the whole time . . . like a steam-engine. Full steam pressure all the time to increase, multiply, and replenish the earth. Spinning out her destiny in record time. . . . She glanced up at the mantelpiece to see the clock . . . . She should make her mind resolute to burn that photograph. . . . It was merely a sigh for a lost slim figure, pretty face, and a curly mass of brown hair. If she went to a dance there wouldn't be many boys nosing around her now . . . . Eight years of it had skimmed the cream out of her life. . . . It was only alone now and in the dark that she could dance before the stars.

She heard the drowsy and querulous voice of her husband asking her if she was coming to bed or going to sit up all night. "Just arranging the clothes for the night," she said. "For Christ's sake, come to bed, woman, and put out the light; impossible for anyone to sleep with that lamp burning on the table!"

Rising she turned the back of the chair to the fire, and replaced the damp clothes over it. Then she undressed down to her chemise, went over to the lamp, turned the wick down as low as possible, and with a vigorous puff put out the flame. She pulled the clothes on the bed down a little and thrust her feet in under them.

"Get in quietly now," grumbled her husband, "and don't slap yourself down as if no one occupied the bed but yourself."

She pushed her legs down cautiously, and gradually separated the four pairs of legs at the end of the bed to make room for her own feet, and lay on her side with her arm around her youngest and her back to her husband, stretched crookedly so as to occupy as little as possible of the bed, and to fit in comfortably at the same time. She remained motionless, every muscle aching in a dull way. Her mind was vaguely painful and clogged against free or clear thought by the heavy, dull, jading work of the day that was over. What she wanted now was rest . . . rest . . . and . . . sleep . . . sleep and rest . . . till six o'clock to-morrow morning. Deli . . . cious to be . . . in bed . . . and ge . . . get to sleep, to ge . . . get to slee. . . . Dimly she felt an arm sliding around her waist . . . and a leg lifted across her body. . . . She tried to shake the leg away, and unfasten the arm that was clinging around her waist. . . . But the hold tightened, and she felt herself being turned over and over on her back. . . . "No, no, Jack, not to-night . . . too tired for that sort of business. . . . Give it over, give it over, Jack. . . ." She tried to plunge away from him, and one of the kids at the bottom of the bed yelled in fright and pain as her toes ploughed his thigh. "Shut up, there, you!" she heard her husband say viciously to the kid, "or I'll leather hell into your hide!" She struggled sleepily and wearily against him so as to hang on to a little rest, for it wasn't fair for him to bully her into his embraces when she was so tired, tired, tired. . . He sank his fingers into the flesh of her shoulders and roughly held her from moving. . . . "Keep quiet for a few moments, can't you?" he said. . . .

She yielded to him in weariness and from habit as she lay stretched on her back; her sleepy eyes opened and she saw the star that had seen her dancing gleaming grandly down at her through the window of the skylight.

THE JOB

SHE watched his head bending over his desk, lifted now and again to glance at her approvingly. She knew she looked enticing in her well-cut tailor suit. Her slim legs were catching his eye. She leaned back in her chair and crossed one over the other. He stretched his hand for some papers at the end of the desk, but she knew that he sought an opportunity to see for a moment a fuller vision of things that stirred him. She suddenly sat straight and uncrossed her legs, for she remembered that her cami-knickers weren't as fresh as she'd like them to be. Idleness had left her no money for laundry, and she had worn one pair after another till she was now wearing the last pair that was in any way presentable. The others had been washed and were waiting to be ironed, but she had been too lazy to finish them off. She should have finished them a week ago, but she had put it off from day to day because she was too tired each

106

day, or too lazy. But, then, look at the time she spent going from audition to agent, and from agent to audition, so that when she got home she was always too tired to do anything. She wanted a job; she must get a job soon or things would be too bad to bear. The rent—there was the rent due. The grocer wouldn't let her go on much longer—he was beginning to threaten already. Her mind was tired out thinking of them. Everywhere she went she carried her anxiety about with her. But it must be kept hidden. She must be free from care and bright when she spoke to managers, or sang and danced at auditions. She hadn't done too badly to-day. If she could only forget the rent and the grocer. She had danced and she had sung before one tall, thin, tremulous man, and two others, puffy-eyed, balloon-bellied money-cuddlers, and had been selected among fifty from a hundred others. Then she had sung again, and had danced again, and had been selected among twenty from the fifty girls. That was something that held a little hope. The grocer's book was red, a red book with the name in gold letters on the cover. Six pounds fourteen and eightpence, that was all; it really wasn't a great deal to owe. Oh, it was more, though; she hadn't counted in what she had got this

week. Three, five and sixpence—seven and
ninepence; ten shillings would more than cover
the lot. Ten and fourteen—seven pounds four
and eightpence; no, it wasn't a big debt. When
she got work, she wouldn't be long paying it off
—all, the whole lot—rent, grocer, and everything. The milkman's book was blue-royal or
navy blue, she couldn't exactly say which.
Curious the colours they liked; one blue, the
other red. No, she didn't remember seeing a
green book. Oh, yes; where she had lived last,
the fishmonger had issued green books to his
customers. Sixteen were to be engaged from
the twenty chosen; sixteen only. Pity they
didn't want the twenty, then the job would be
sure. After all, twenty wasn't a lot to take on,
the few additional pounds wouldn't break them.
They were a mean crowd, these theatrical producers; wanted a hell of a lot for their money.
Pretty face; well-shaped legs; good figure;
clever dancing; fair voice, all the better if it was
good; agility, stamina, patience, and personality.
Oh, yes; personality was very important.
Didn't want much; just a little more than what
you'd go to church with. If luck came her way,
she was sure the show would go for at least five
weeks. Four pounds for five weeks would be
twenty pounds. Not much, but enough to

108

scrape her out of debt. It might run for ten weeks, might be a success and run for a year, right through for a whole year. Nothing like putting a halo round a hope. It would mean two hundred pounds for her. That would bring her liberty to get some things she sorely needed, if she was to keep up appearances, and appearances counted a lot when you were looking for a job. She wouldn't want for a fresh petticoat or dainty cami-knickers for a special occasion— when she went out to a dance with Jim, for instance.

Pity Jim wasn't one of these managers or producers. Why wasn't he this one here, sitting at his desk eyeing her legs? But if that were so, it would be the other way round, and this manager would be Jim, so that would make a difference the same thing. What was she thinking of? Her mind was really getting muddled. She must bring it on to the things immediately in front of her. She would soon have to fence, and very shortly she might have to fight. So she must keep her mind clear. Jim would be calling for her to-night at eight; they were to have a little snack in her place, and then go off together to a dance. And all the work she had before her yet, to make an alteration in her dance frock, and to iron and arrange her undies.

It was annoying that this fellow should still keep her waiting. Pretending to be looking through his papers while he was eyeing her thoughtfully and glancing at her legs. During the last few years he must have seen hundreds and hundreds of legs, and ought to be a little tired of them now. It was something else; some funny, peculiar, unusual motion or twist of her body; a look on her face or in her eyes, or even the way she moved her hands that drew his attention to her.

How he twisted and rustled his hands through his papers. He would soon want to be twisting and rustling them through her—she felt it. Well, not yet, sir, anyhow; she would have to think it out a little first. If he tried, however, she wouldn't make a great fuss. She would put him off, fence him, and wait till she was sure, or nearly sure, that it was worth while. When she saw him whispering to his two companions, she knew he was whispering about her. She fancied faithfully all he said : she had stuff in her ; didn't they think so? Graceful. . . . Oh, lively too. Would he mark her down among the twenty? And she was marked down among the twenty, so here she was sitting before him, and he was eyeing her legs . . . and twisting and rustling his hands through the papers on his desk. She wished he would say what he had to say, and let her go. It would take her all her time to be ready when Jim called for her. This old buffer in front of her didn't care, didn't even know. It was a month or more now since she had had a dance, and if the old man didn't soon make a move, she'd have to rush things.

If she went with Jim to-night, she'd have to be careful not to let him go too far. Oh, dear, she had to be careful of everyone. Careful of Jim because he was too poor; and careful of this old buffer because he was too rich. Careful of Jim because she wanted to give herself to him, and careful of the other because she didn't want to give herself to him. It was a curious world. . . . It was easier to put Jim off than this one. Jim was young and poor, and could wait; this one was impatient and rich, and she wanted the job. She knew that this old gilded pig couldn't really enjoy or understand the companionship of girls. He brought them to dinner or supper just to fill in the time before he asked them to take their clothes off. Jim could do that too, but clothes on or clothes off, supper was supper to Jim, and a dance was a jolly exciting passage of time. His love-making was brisk and fresh, with nothing stealthy in it; there was fear and shyness in it, but there was no shame. Here there was fear, no shyness, and a good deal of shame. But she was bound to meet this sort of thing sooner or later, and she would have to put up with it and go careful. . . . She heard him speaking to her. . . . "You didn't do badly, dear . . . you showed promise, distinct promise. . . . Dancing good, very good indeed, and singing not bad at all. . . . It's a toss-up between you and Miss Brierly. . . . Hanley favours her, but it can be wangled . . . we'll wangle it, never fear. . . . Show's going to be a sure thing. . . . Keep at it, and you never know. . . . Understudy for a little and then, perhaps . . . leading lady. You're as good as there, my dear. . . . First rehearsal next Friday, ten o'clock sharp. . . ." How like a tumbling jelly he looked when he stood up. . . . She didn't want him to tell her that the brooch in her breast was a pretty one. A lot she cared whether he thought the brooch pretty or not. . . . He could see right well that the little rubies were real without fingering them. . . . A lot he cared whether they were real or not. . . . Jabbing his fingers into her bosom, and talking about the shape of the brooch, as if she didn't know what he was up to. And look at his picture, do, dear, do. . . . Painted by someone that wanted work badly. His smug, smiling, smutty face looking like a first-fruit of

God's creation. . . . If she had a face like that she might get it photoed, but she'd think twice before she got it painted. Beside a table piled with papers and his hand on an open book. . . . Good idea, the bust of Shakespeare at one end of the table. . . . With his knee pressing against her thigh while he was telling her about it, and showing her where the picture was particularly good. . . . The look of deity-tinged irritation that came to his face when she inched away from him. . . . "Good-bye, and thanks" . . . the way he held her hand. . . . Take supper with him to-night. . . . Indeed. Wanted to start off at once. . . . Come along please, you mustn't keep me waiting. . . . Cheek of these men. . . . Open their arms and expect you to jump into them. . . . Bring his car round for her. . . . No thanks. . . . Wait till she got her job first. . . . Tuesday. . . . Sorry, engaged. . . . Oh, Wednesday night, then. . . . All right, Wednesday. . . . Good-bye. . . . It was something to be breathing the air even of Piccadilly again after that sombre, stuffy, sinister-looking torture-chamber of an office. . . . Wanted a lot for four pounds a week. . . . Little enough for work that sweated her for hours every night without having to let herself be mauled about into the bargain. She wished she was a little better at that kind of game. She could make quite a lot out of it if she wasn't so damned shy. Somehow or other she couldn't make use of it as other girls did. No good at a business deal. She'd try this time, anyhow; everyone had to learn, and after a little practice she'd get going all right. How to start, that was the difficulty. . . . She might hint that she owed some rent. No, that would be too common. She'd have to find a fairer way than that. . . . The look that fellow gave her when she was passing; thought she was another kind of woman. . . . Wonderful the number of men that do nothing but prowl, prowl, prowl for women. . . . One thing, she'd have to hold him off for a time, job or no job. A woman shrinks in the mind of a man when he swings her easily into his arms. She was sorry now she accepted his offer to supper on Wednesday. Should she put him off a little longer? Wednesday? Oh, no, couldn't; sorry; full up the whole week. Something on every night. Every night? Every night, my dear man; sorry. Next week, maybe; ring me up some evening and we'll see. Instead of that she hesitated, stammered, and gave him Wednesday. How is it she couldn't do these things properly, like other girls? Some kink in her somewhere. . . . A quiet little restaurant that

he occasionally goes to. Fancy that now. A
quiet place, to have an unquiet time of it. She'd
go to an unquiet place to have a quiet time,
or she'd go nowhere. She wouldn't let him
handle as much joy out of her as he thought for
a job that she had not got yet. If he really
wanted to get going, it would cost him a lot
more than four pounds a week. She must
decide upon a definite line of action between
this and Wednesday night. Wednesday's a
good way off, however, and to-night will be full
of hours of dance and joy with Jim.

Curious that there was hardly a part of London
in which you could slide out of view of a tree.
It was nice to see London plumed here and there
with a tree, though Leicester Square hadn't
the cool, rich look of the other London squares.
Looked rather like a roof-garden that had been
taken down and planted carefully in the streets.
Wonder what the trees are that grow there.
Wouldn't know them even if she knew. She'd
know a holly-tree anywhere, and could guess at
an oak because of its funny leaves, and because
she had read when she was a kid so much about
it hiding a Harry, or an Edward, or Charlie in its
branches at Boscobel. Mahogany must be a
lovely-looking tree, but it couldn't grow here.
But she had other things to think about besides

trees. . . . As soon as she was a little flush the first next thing she'd buy would be a brassiere. The one she had was going west, creased and uncomfortable; no use to her figure for it had lost all its resiliency, as the motorists say. Pity she couldn't ask Jim to buy her a brassiere instead of a few handkerchiefs. Or the manager—God, imagine her asking the manager to buy her a brassiere! He'd rush one to her and want to try it on to see if it would fit. Jim would want to do that too. A man needs to give very little to get big ideas rushing into his head. To be, or not to be a brassiere, that's the question. Strange if she met a bee buzzing along round Piccadilly Circus. . . . A bee buzzing along to buy a brassiere. . . . What she wanted wasn't a bee, but a bus buzzing along to bring her home. There was her bus just starting. Just like her to buzz in on top of a rush-hour crowd. . . . She'd have to push, shove, and fight if she didn't want to be kept for half an hour. . . . Here was one coming again, now. . . . Push . . . pull . . . and sho-o-ve! Here she was on the top with a nice fresh breeze blowing. The look on the fat one's face when she skidded out of the way. Don't knock her down, please. It was a mercy from God that most people one met were strangers to each other.

To-night she would leave anxiety and fear and

troubling thoughts alone and apart for a while in
Jim's arms, responding in every nerve of her
body and every motion of her mind to the blood-
enflaming rhythms of the drum, fiddle, and saxo-
phone.   She could see the gaily coloured lights
gleaming already.   And feel the arms of Jim
clasping her.   And the boys and the girls swaying softly, turning gently, wriggling closer together, moving, moving, moving along. . . . How
these buses crawl along. . . . Brrrum tumtum-
tumtumbrrrumtum brrrumtumtum tootle tootle
lootootleloo tootletoo brrrum looloo tootle loo. . . .
Glorious, Jim, isn't it? . . . tootle loo loo tootle
loo. . . . Clasp me closer, clasp me closer, clasp,
clasp closer. . . . Brrrum loo loo tootle loo. . . .

At her door she was at last.   Slipped into the
bottom of her bag again, her key. . . . Irritate a
saint.   Not a great measure of time left now to
get everything ready.   Get the iron, get the
iron. . . . Mauve or green or cream-coloured
undies, which would she put on?   The green
would look sweet under the tulle of her black
skirt. . . . They would blend harmoniously in the
swing of the dance, and do delightfully. . . . Now
we're well away. . . . Tootle, tootle brrum loo loo
tootle loo. . . . She'd dance to-night; miss only
what would pass in the time of taking a sandwich
and a glass of wine. . . . She'd just about be able

to get everything ready before Jim would come
to hurry her, happy-faced, off to the labour and
joy of the dance. . . . She'd see the tensing look on
Jim's face when he felt the motion of her legs in
the movements of the dance. . . . Tootle loo loo
loo tootle loo.   There's the postman . . . a telegram. . . . No answer, boy. . . . She went in and
read it again, slowly and tensely. . . . "Mother
and Dad up in town for a few days.   Everything
off to-night.   Arranged another dance for
Wednesday night love Jim." . . . She sent the
iron flying into a far corner with a vicious swing,
and clenched and crushed the green cami-
knickers in her hands, and her lips quivered as
she sat silent.

A FALL IN A GENTLE
WIND

A FALL IN A GENTLE WIND

MOLLSER sat motionless on a deal chair placed on the five-step landing fronting the widely open door of a tenement house. It was a lovely day in late spring—glory be to God! The sun was shining gorgeously, streaming through the dismal avenue of glowering houses; its rays were ignorantly gilding the sordid street and degenerate pathways with a radiant, caressing, golden glow; softly burnishing into a vivid gleam each of the age-worn grimy windows, and touching with a shimmering newness the tattered remnants of cotton lace that curtained them, and sought to veil from the timid passer-by the haggard, mournful life that crawled or scratched or tossed itself into mechanical motion within the secretive chambers of the slum.

A tremulous shiver passed through Mollser's couched body, as she mistily seemed to see a sinister vitality gleaming from the eye-like windows, leering down on the fibrous life that tottered into or plodded out of the various cave-like hallways. They seemed to glance in a side-long, jeering manner at the horde of uncared-for youngsters playing feverishly in the street, as if conscious that each slum was a secondary parent to them, each child subdued by one faith and one baptism, having had to pass through the womb of the slum when they had been safely delivered from the womb of the mother. Having been born first in the image of God, they were afterwards to be moulded in the image of the Devil.

Mollser shivered again, for the tenement opposite, a foul, wrinkled, dishevelled, palsied-looking building, like a worn-out harlot, seemed to be muttering across to her.

"Well, Mollser, how are you to-day; going along well, ay? You're a credit to number fifteen. . . . All the little body's a mass of tuber-cular rot. . . . Feeling as if you'd like to be laid out? Time enough, time enough, little one. . . . We'll give you a long spell on the broad of your back before we pack you away in the coffin. . . . You're the little masterpiece of number fifteen . . . . Each of us has its own. . . . Mine went a week ago. . . . But I've years of fertility left in me still, and there's many more to come. . . . My own little one above with spinal disease, in a few months, 'll be able to hold her own with the best of you. . . . We've a rich and lush heritage for all our children, and it will go hard with us to disinherit any."

"Christ help us!" murmured Mollser, closing her brown eyes, to shut out the vision of the leering threat that glowered in front of her, and turning her head to deflect from her dim soul the murmur she heard but could not understand.

Dreamily she heard the muffled shout of the playing children, punctuated by the vehement blasts from the horns of the passing motors, the drivers worming their way with sullen faces through the forms darting about in a frenzy of animal unconsciousness.

"Harps, sixpence," bawled a voice to her right, followed by "Heads, thruppence; harps, a wing." "For Christ's sake, keep back there, an' give a fella a chance to toss th' coins."

"The toss school is on again," thought Mollser; "that's Jimmy Byrne's voice: he must ha' got th' dole to-day, an' he'll be bringin' Mary Timmins to th' pictures to-night, if he doesn't get too dhrunk. . . . He must be motting her now, for six months. Curious, a sturdy fella like him to be gone on a bloodless one like Mary Timmins. . . ." Mollser instinctively looked at her own hands, pallid with the mournful delicacy of disease. . . . "The summer may work wonders," thought Mollser, "and then——"

Interrupted in her thoughts by shuffling steps coming from the hall behind her, Mollser moodily watched Granny Hennessy climbing stiffly down the five steps as if they were a precipitous cliff, her skinny hands holding fearfully to the railings, her tiny bluey lips aquiver, muttering resentfully as she shambled along : "Holy Virgin, it's nearly time we had a bit of sun. The draughts in that bloody house 'ud skin you. . . . I'm goin' for me oul' age pension; nine shillin's now, only nine shillin's now. Takin' a lousy shillin' off a poor oul' woman. . . . A lousy shillin'. . . . A lousy oul' shillin'."

A rollicking twittering, having in it the lilt of joyous intoxication, roused up Mollser to raise her head, and, shaking back with a feminine swing her shock of dark hair, dimmed with the dirt of street and tenement, she saw a pair of sparrows abandoning themselves to the joy of tumultuous motion in the bosom of one of the little trees that stood at regular distances apart, surrounded by crudely cut wooden palings, along the pathway's edge of the slum street. A vague sense of kinship moved her to sympathy as she looked at the frail, thin trunk, like her own shrinking body; the fragile branches stretching towards the sky as if appealing for deliverance; the leaves murmuring a gentle protest, and the whole nature of the little captive from the wood, pregnant with bewilderment at the loss of its heritage of solitude, and the intimate caresses of sun and shower that had lost their purity and power.

A half-hidden gleam of subconscious envy faintly glimmered from the brown, wistful eyes of Mollser as she watched the animated excitement of the little leaves sharing in the motions of the sparrows springing with an exultant celerity from spray to spray; she gently thrilled as she noticed the rapid pulsing movement of their little throats, chirruping with the recklessness of elemental vigour, their tiny, diamond-like eyes, luminous with the confident hilarity of a natural discipline that gave them the fulness of life.

And Mollser shivered as she vaguely thought that life was more abundant in a common sparrow than it was in her: song and rhythm and motion, against weakness, disease, and death, a fragile feathered morsel of life, that even her little, wasted hand could clutch and banish from the universe, vibrant with the vigour that her body, passive because of tubercular weakness, would never know, and gone, too, for ever from the life that lingered in the coiled-up frame of little Alice Tait opposite, gripped in the Laocoon vice of creeping paralysis.

Like a warning gong the voice of her mother sounded in her ear from the area below: "Keep th' shawl well wrapped round you, Mollser. . . . If you get another chill in your chest, you'll be havin' me stoppin' up all night with you, an' turnin' your father into a divil with th' coughin' keepin' him awake at night."

Mollser tightened her shawl round her, and, like the mechanical swing of a weathercock yielding to a swooning wind, she turned her head and looked down with a dull interest on her mother below, gathering from a frayed and frequently joined line, stretching precariously from one end of the area to the other, the week's washing that had been hung out to dry, and was now to be ironed and made ready to wear on the Sabbath that was made for men.

She saw, one by one, the pitiable articles carefully collected into the gnarled hands of her mother: her own little shift, of flannelette, its once brightly pink stripes faded into dim, unhealthy-looking lines; her mother's, tawny-coloured with constant wear, encouraged to live a little longer by the company of a multitude of patches; her artificial *crêpe de chine* blouse, with its saucy glad neck, that long long ago had prompted Jimmy Byrne to dance and dance with her, now bereft of all its glory; one of the two sheets that protected them grudgingly from the shaggy coverings of old coats and sugar sacks; a few pairs of socks living their last days, and her father's cotton shirt, with the hole under the arm growing larger and larger week by week. Her mother gathered carefully lest a thoughtless pull might rip the last remnant of life out of them, and, pressing them maternally against her bosom, looked up at Mollser, a faint smile trying to alleviate her misery-mangled face, and muttered monotonously: "Kippers to-night, Mollser; full week of th' dole he got, an' we have kippers to-night—one for him and one between me and you."

The clang of the bell shook a start out of Mollser: one, two, three, then a pause; twice three again, and a pause, then nine slow strokes—it was the Angelus. She noticed the men sitting on the steps taking off their hats and whipping the pipes out of their mouths as they bent their heads. Mollser inclined her head and murmured an Ave Maria.

Lithe-limbed spring had ripened into a pompous full-bodied summer. The dingy street sparkled in the golden robe of the sun. The

tenements pantingly leaned against each other
for mutual support; their open windows and gaping doors seemed to be gasping for breath.
Everything seemed to be struggling in a sea of
warmth. The passing traffic glided indolently
by; children lounged lazily on the paths, or
dreamily nursed worn-out toys on their laps as
they sat on the stone steps of the houses. The
groups of men and women had sought the shade
of the doorway and the hall. The foliage of the
exiled trees drooped languidly in the heated
stillness.

Up in the one-room tenancy of the Conway's,
Mollser, rapidly breathing, lay in the bed that
had given a harassed rest to her mother, father,
and herself for many years. She could see the
ceiling, cracked and tremulous with the pounding
of the family overhead breaking sticks or smash-
ing coal. How vividly the picture of the Sacred
Heart glowed on the ghastly whiteness of the
whitewashed wall! On the hob was the poor
little kettle that had to do so much work. And
the dresser, the biggest thing in the room, standing proudly with its back to the wall, consciously
displaying its array of rugged delph, garnered
through many years by the systematic barter of
piles of rags and innumerable bottles. She
could hear the little clock on the mantelpiece

ticking the minutes away with a hoarse impatience. The little table, always covered with a page of newspaper when they were taking a meal. . . . Mollser looked at her father, divested of his coat, looked fixedly from the open window into the street. She heard the swish of the brush her mother was using to wash down the lobby outside, and the soft splashing of her hands into the bucket that held the day's supply of water for drinking and cooking purposes, and in which her father every morning washed his face with a fantasia of blowing, and his feet on the first Sunday of every month.

There had been a strange quietness in the room for the past few hours or days—she could not tell which. Some way or another she didn't like the silent kisses her mother occasionally gave her. Her father, talkative enough, had stilled his tongue, and rapped his pipe, when it needed refilling, against the hob or on the window sill with a fierceness that seemed to drum a rally to some idea that had found a lodging in his mind.

The nuns had been with her yesterday: she still saw their fading image in the mirror of pre-consciousness. The black-robed figures standing beside her bed. The heavy, brass crucifixes, decorations of the Church Militant, glittering

on their bosoms. Their faces sheathed safely
within the deep shelter of their spathe-like
bonnets. They had talked of the goodness of
God, of the mercy of Christ, and of the Faith of
the Little Flower. . . . She had heard an authori-
tative murmur outside the door, divided by her
mother: "Yes, Sister" . . . "No, Sister" . . .
"Yes, Sister . . ." faintly audible as they
descended the first flight of stairs. . . . She
didn't like the nuns to come: somehow they
seemed to leave dark shadows behind them that
continually hovered over her head. If she had
the power in her to get up and go for a walk it
would do her good. She felt better . . . maybe,
to-morrow . . .

The door of the room opened, and her
mother came in, hurriedly and agitated, followed by two big men wearing vivid red shirts,
carrying something between them. Her father
rose to his feet, clapped his pipe into his pocket,
and rigidly stood staring at them. Her mother
came to the bed, and bending over her whispered: "Here's the men, Mollser, with th'
stretcher to bring you to the Hospice. . . .
You'll be well looked afther be th' nuns, an' if it
is God's will, you'll get all right again."

The Hospice . . . the Hospice for the Dying!
That's where they wanted to bring her . . . she

130

wouldn't go. She wouldn't go! She felt better—she knew she was better—and even if she
wasn't, a week longer where she was—even one
more day to linger longingly by the side of hope.

The nuns! What did the nuns know? They
were always dying to be sending souls safely to
Paradise or Purgatory!

"Mother, I can't go, I can't go there; I won't
go," She painfully struggled to the far side of
the bed, her bloodless hands twitching at the
bedclothes, her shift, open at the breast, showing
the wan weakness of her chest, revealing one
breast that had subsided to a crinkled blob, the
nipple, against the ghastly pallor of the skin,
gleaming like the red of a cherry.

"It's th' only place for you," muttered her
father. "You can get nothin' you want here;
th' pair of us is worn out watchin' an' attendin'
you. . . . It's nearly time you had a little thought
of your mother. . . ."

Gently, the huge, red-shirted men lifted her,
motionless and lost, on to the stretcher. She
felt herself carried slowly, slowly down the
gloomy, dirty stairs, out into the strength-
quivering sun, through a group of staring, silent
women and children, into the ambulance standing at the side of the street, the throbbing
engine giving it the vibration of a living thing

excitedly eager to carry her away to the dreadful place of shrinking shadows.

Shawled and wordless, her mother climbed in and sat beside the stretcher. Mollser sidled her hand over till it touched her mother's; she felt a gentle, agonizing pressure that set her body quivering. As if from an infinite distance, she heard the murmur of voices: "Harps a tanner" . . . "Heads a bob" . . . "For Christ's sake, keep back there, and give a fella a chance to toss th' coins."

With a gliding spring, the motor moved away.

FALLS IN AN IDLE WIND

THE END OF THE BEGINNING

A Comedy in One Act

K

CHARACTERS

DARRY BERRILL. *About fifty-five; stocky, obstinate, with a pretty big belly. He is completely bald, except for a tuft of grey hair just above the forehead.*

BARRY DERRILL, *Darry's neighbour. Same age as Darry. Thin, easy-going, big moustache, and is very near-sighted.*

LIZZIE BERRILL, *Darry's wife. About forty-five. A good woman about the house, but that's about all.*

Scene: *A big comfortable kitchen. Steep stairs, almost like a ladder, leading to upper room, top right. Huge fireplace, right. Some chairs, one heavy, with rubbered castors. Small settee, and table. Chest of drawers, left, on top of which stands a gramophone. Door back, and to left of door a window. To right of door, a dresser, on which is, as well as delf, a large clock of the alarm type. To right of dresser, on a nail, hangs a whip; to the left of dresser hangs a mandolin. On table, a quantity of unwashed delf. To right of fireplace, a lumber room. The room, at night, is lighted by an electric bulb, hanging from centre of ceiling. It is a fine early autumn evening, with the sun low in the heavens. On wall, back, a large red card on which "Do It Now" is written in white letters. A sink under the window.*

DARRY (*at door of room above. He is shaving, and his chin is covered with lather*). This shaving

137

water's dead cold, woman. D'ye hear me?
This shaving water's dead cold.

LIZZIE (*busy about the room—quietly*). Come
down and heat it, then.

DARRY (*scornfully*). Too much to do, I suppose. I'd do all that has to be done here, three
times over, 'n when all was finished, I'd be sigh-
ing for something to do.

LIZZIE. If you had half of what I have to do
here, at the end of the evening you'd be picked
up dead out of the debris.

DARRY. I would?

LIZZIE. You would.

DARRY. Sure?

LIZZIE. Certain.

DARRY. If I only had half to do?

LIZZIE. Or less.

DARRY. I'd be picked up out of the debris?

LIZZIE. Out of the middle of it.

DARRY. Dead?

LIZZIE. As a mackerel.

DARRY (*fiercely*). I'm always challenging you
to change places for a few hours, but you won't do
it. I'd show you what a sinecure of a job you
had here, while I'm sweating out in the fields.

LIZZIE. Go out 'n finish the mowing of the
meadow. It'll take you only half an hour or so,
'n there's plenty of light in the sky still.

THE END OF THE BEGINNING

DARRY (*who has been shaving himself during this argument*). The meadow'll do to be done to-morrow. Why don't you let me do what's to be done in the house, an' you go 'n mow the meadow? Why don't you do that? 'don't you do that? 'you do that? Agony to look at you; agony to listen to you; agony, agony to be anywhere near you.

LIZZIE. I'd just like to see you doing what's to be done about the house—I'd just like to see you.

DARRY. What is there to be done about the house—will you tell us that?

LIZZIE. There's the pig 'n the heifer 'n the hens to be fed 'n tended. There's ironing, cooking, washing, 'n sewing to be done.

DARRY. Sewing! An' only a button back 'n front of me so that it's next thing to a miracle that my trousers are kept from starting the neighbours talking.

LIZZIE. If you say much more, I'll go 'n mow the meadow, 'n leave you to see what you can make of the house-work.

DARRY (*angrily*). Buzz off, buzz off, then, an' I'll show you how the work of a house is done. Done quietly; done with speed, 'n without a whisper of fuss in its doing. Buzz off, if you want to, 'n I'll show you 'n all your sex how the work of a house is done!

(LIZZIE *violently pulls off a jazz-coloured
overall she is wearing, and flings it on
the floor.*)

LIZZIE (*furiously*). Put that on you, then, 'n do
what remains to be done about the house, while
I go an' mow the meadow. Get into it, 'n show
the world an' your poor wife the wonders you
can do when you're under a woman's overall.

DARRY (*a little frightened*). Oh, I'll manage all
right.

LIZZIE. An' don't you let that Alice Lanigan
in here while I'm away either, d'ye hear?

DARRY. What Alice Lanigan?

LIZZIE (*in a temper*). What Alice Lanigan!
The Alice Lanigan I caught you chattering to
yesterday, when you should have been mowing
the meadow. The Alice Lanigan that's setting
you on to nag at me about the little I have to do
in the house. The Alice Lanigan that's goad-
ing you into the idea that if you were a little
slimmer round the belly, you'd be a shevaleer,
an's getting you to do physical jerks. The
Alice Lanigan that's on the margin of fifty, 'n
assembles herself together as if she was a girl
in her teens, jutting out her bust when she's
coming in, 'n jutting out her behind when she's
going out, like the Lady of Shalott, to catch the
men—that's the Alice Lanigan I mean.

DARRY. I don't be thinking of Alice Lanigan.

LIZZIE. I've seen you, when you thought I slumbered 'n slep, naked, with nothing at all on you, doing your physical jerks in front of the looking-glass, 'n that, too, when the lessons of a Mission were still hot in your heart—an all for Alice Lanigan. Maybe you don't know that she has a kid who has never had a pat on the head from a father.

DARRY. You buzz off now, 'n I'll show how the work of a house is done.

LIZZIE (*while she is putting a broad-brimmed hat on her head, pulling a pair of old gloves over her hands, and taking down a whip hanging from a nail in the wall*). I'm telling you it's a dangerous thing to shake hands with Alice Lanigan, even with a priest giving the introduction. The day'll come soon when you'll know she's making mechanical toys of you 'n that other old fool, Barry Derrill, who's so near-sighted that he can't see the sky, unless the moon's shining in it!

DARRY. Cheerio.

LIZZIE (*at the door*). I'm going now, 'n we'll see how you do the work of the house.

DARRY. Hail 'n farewell to you. An' mind you, this'll be only the beginning of things.

LIZZIE. God grant that it won't be the end,

141

an' that when I come back, I'll at least find the four walls standing.

> (*She goes out.* DARRY *strolls to the door,
> and watches her going down the road.*)

DARRY (*scornfully to himself*). Mow the meadow! Well, let her see her folly out.

> (*As he shuts the door, the clock in the dis-
> tant Town Hall strikes eight,* DARRY
> *returns, glances at the clock on the
> dresser, notices that it has stopped, takes
> it up, puts his ear against it, shakes it,
> begins to wind it, finds it difficult to turn,
> puts added strength into the turning, and
> a whirring rattle, like a strong spring
> breaking, comes from the inside of the
> clock. He hastily replaces the clock on the
> dresser. After a few seconds' thought,
> he takes it up again, removes the back,
> and part of a big, broken spring darts out,
> which he hurriedly crams in again, and
> puts the clock back on the dresser.*)

DARRY. Lizzie again!

> (*He catches sight of the gramophone, looks
> at it, thinks for a second, goes over to the
> chest of drawers, takes some records from
> behind it and fixes one on the disc of the
> gramophone. He takes off his waist-
> coat, loosens his braces, stands stiff,*

142

strokes his thighs, pats his belly, and tries
to push it back a little. He starts the
gramophone going, runs to the centre of
the room, and lies down on the broad of
his back. The gramophone begins to
give directions for physical exercises, to
which DARRY *listens and, awkwardly,*
clumsily, and puffingly, tries to follow the
movements detailed in the words spoken
by the gramophone when the music
commences.)

GRAMOPHONE. Lie on back; hands behind the
head; feet together—are you ready? Bend the
right knee; draw it into the waistline, towards
the chest—commence!

(DARRY *is too slow, or the gramophone is*
too quick, for he can't keep up with the
time of the music. When he finds that
he is behind the time of the music, DARRY
increases his speed by partial performance
of the movements, and so gets into touch
with the time, but presently, blowing and
panting, he is out of time again by a beat
or two. He climbs stiffly on to his feet,
goes over to gramophone, and puts the
indicator to "Slow.")

DARRY. Phuh. Too quick, too damn quick
altogether.

143

(*He starts the gramophone going, runs to
the centre of the room, and again lies
down on the broad of his back. When
the music begins he goes through the
movements as before; but the music is
playing so slowly now that he finds it
impossible to go slowly enough to keep to
the time of the tune. When he finds
himself in front of a beat, he stops and
puffs and waits for the beat to catch up
with him before he recommences. As he
is going through these movements, the
door opens, and* BARRY DERRILL *comes
into the room. He has a mandolin
under his arm, and is wearing wide-
rimmed, thick-lensed spectacles.*)

BARRY (*briskly*). Come 'n kiss me sweet 'n
twenty—what the hell are you trying to do?

DARRY. Can't you see what I'm trying to do?
Take off your spectacles 'n get a closer look.
Keeping meself fit 'n flexible—that's what I'm
trying to do.

BARRY. The rhythm's too slow, man; tense
your muscles; you're not tun'd into the movements properly, man.

DARRY. The indicator must have shifted.
Slip over 'n put it to the point marked medium,
'n then get down here 'n give us a hand.

BARRY. What about the prologue of playing the song we're to sing at the Town Hall concert?

DARRY. Get down 'n have five minutes of this, first; we'll both sing the better for it.

BARRY (*dubiously*). Never done it to music, 'n I wouldn't be able to keep in touch with the, with the measure.

DARRY. The music makes it easier, man. Keep your eye on me, 'n move when I move.

(BARRY *reluctantly takes off his coat and waistcoat, goes over to the gramophone, puts his nose against the instrument, and puts the indicator to "Fast.*")

DARRY. To do this thing properly you'd want to be wearing shorts. Right; now keep in touch with the rhythm, or you'll mar everything. Start her off, and stretch yourself down.

(BARRY *starts the gramophone, runs over and lies down opposite to* DARRY, *so that the soles of their feet are only a few inches apart.*

GRAMOPHONE (*very rapidly*). Lie on back; hands behind the head; feet together—are you ready? Bend the right knee; draw it into the waistline towards the chest; breathe out—commence!

(*The tempo of the tune forces them to do the exercises in a frantic way, till it dawns*

> on DARRY, *who is nearly exhausted, that
> there's something wrong. He stops while*
> BARRY *goes on manfully.*)

DARRY (*scornfully*). Eh, eh, there, wait a minute, wait a minute, man. Don't you see anything wrong?

BARRY (*stopping*). No; what's wrong?

DARRY (*testily*). Aw, what's wrong! We're congestin' ourselves with speed; that's what's wrong. You must have jammed the indicator hard to Fast. (*He gets up, goes to the gramophone, and puts it right.*) We're entertainin' ourselves, Barry, an' not tryin' to say the Rosary.

> (*He comes back and stretches himself again
> on the floor. The music begins and the
> two men commence the exercises. After
> a few moments,* DARRY *slows down a
> little, misses several beats, and tries to
> blame* BARRY.)

DARRY (*excitedly keeping up the movements, but out of time, as he talks*). Try to keep the proper rhythm up, man. (*He hums the tune of "Coming thro' the Rye."*) Dad th' didee dah th' diddy dah th' diddy dee—that way man. Dah th' diddy dah th' diddy (*rapidly*). Keep your eye on me. Dah th' diddy dee.

> (*After a few movements* DARRY *is out of
> time and breathless; he stops and sits up*

146

> *to complain, but he really wants to get
> a rest.*)

DARRY (*with aggravated patience*). Barry,
you're spoiling the whole thing by getting out
of time. Don't let your arms and legs go
limber, tense your muscles. Three beats to the
bar, see? Now!

> (*They start again; DARRY is soon behind
> time, blowing and puffing out of him.
> BARRY keeps to the beat of the tune
> splendidly.*)

DARRY (*angrily*). You're going too damn
quick, altogether, now, man!

BARRY. No I'm not—I'm there to the tick
every time.

DARRY (*violently*). There to the tick—how is
it you're not in the line with me, then, if you're
there to the tick? I don't know whether you're
in front of me or behind me. Are you too stiff
or what?

BARRY. I'm there to the second every time.
It's you that's missin' a beat in the bar.

DARRY (*indignantly, stopping to talk, while
BARRY goes on*). I'm missin' it because I'm
tryin' to foster you into the right balance
'n rhythm of the movements. That's why
I'm missin' it. (*Loudly*) An' I'm wastin' me
time!

147

BARRY (*sharply*). I'm doin' me best, amn't I?

DARRY (*more sharply still*). Your best's a hell of a way behind what's wanted. It's pitiful 'n painful to be watchin' you, man. (*He stands up and looks at* BARRY, *who keeps going.*) Eh, eh, you'll do yourself an injury, Barry. Get up 'n we'll do the song. (*As* BARRY *goes on*) Oh, get up 'n we'll do the song.

> (BARRY *gets up reluctantly, and* DARRY *goes over and stops the gramophone.*)

BARRY. I was doin' it well enough, if you'd let me alone.

DARRY (*scornfully*). Yes; like the Londonderry Air play'd in march time.

> (*They get their mandolins and stand side by side at the back.*)

DARRY. Now we walk in a semicircle down to the front, 'n bow, you remember? Ready?

BARRY. Yep.

DARRY. Go!

> (*They both step off to the right, take a few steps, and then they halt.*)

BARRY. Something wrong; we don't go round the same way, do we?

DARRY (*testily*). Of course there's something wrong; of course we don't go round the same way. Can't you try to remember, Barry? You're to go to the left, to the left.

BARRY. I remember distinctly I was to go to the right.

DARRY (*irritably*). Oh, don't be such an egotist, Barry. Now think for a minute. (*A pause.*) Now make up your mind—d'ye want to go to the left or the right?

BARRY (*testily*). Oh, left, right—any way.

DARRY. Left, then. Go.

> (*They march round, one to the right, the other to the left, meet in the front, and bow.*)

DARRY. You start, Barry, my boy.

BARRY (*singing*).

One summer eve a handsome man met a handsome maiden strolling,

DARRY.

Down where the bees were hummin' an' the wild flowers gaily growing;

BARRY.

Said she we'll sit down here a while, all selfish thoughts controlling,

DARRY.

Down where the bees are hummin' an' the wild flowers gaily growing:

BARRY.

Said she we'll meditate on things, things high 'n edifying,

How all things live 'n have their day 'n end their day by dying.

THE END OF THE BEGINNING

He put his hand on her white breast an' murmur'd life is trying,

DARRY.

Down where the bees are hummin' an' the wild
flowers gaily growing.

BARRY.

The moon glanc'd down 'n wonder'd what the
pair of them were doing,

DARRY.

Down where the bees were hummin' an' the wild
flowers gaily growing;

BARRY.

Then th' moon murmur'd, I feel hot, 'n fear a
storm is brewing,

DARRY.

Down where the bees are hummin' an' the wild
flowers gaily growing.

BARRY.

She talk'd so well of things so high, he started
to reward her,

The moon ran in behind a cloud, for there was
none to guard her.

I'll take that off, she said, you'd ruin the lace
that's round the border,

DARRY.

Down where the bees are hummin' an' the wild
flowers gaily growing.

BARRY.

White-featur'd 'n thin goodie-goodies rush
    around excited,

DARRY.

Down where the bees are hummin' an' the wild
    flowers gaily growing;

BARRY.

Proclaiming that the dignity of living has been
    blighted,

DARRY.

Down where the bees are hummin' an' the wild
    flowers gaily growing.

BARRY.

But when the light is soft 'n dim, discovery dis-
    arming,

The modest moon behind the clouds, young
    maidens, coy 'n charming,

Still cuddle men who cuddle them 'n carry on
    alarming,

DARRY.

Down where the bees are hummin' an' the wild
    flowers gaily growing.

> (*When the song has ended*, DARRY *cocks
> his ear and listens.*)

BARRY. Shall we try it once more?

DARRY. Shush, shut up, can't you?

> (DARRY *goes over to the door, opens it and
> listens intently. There is heard the*

rattling whirr caused by the steady and regular movement of a mowing machine. The distant Town Hall clock strikes nine.)

DARRY (*hastily putting the mandolin away*). I forgot. I'll have to get going.

BARRY. Get going at what?

DARRY. House-work. (*He begins to get into the overall left off by* LIZZIE.) I dared her, an' she left me to do the work of the house while she was mowing the meadow. If it isn't done when she comes back, then sweet good-bye to the status I had in the home. (*He finds it difficult to get the overall on.*) Dih dih dih, where's the back 'n where's the front, 'n which is which is the bottom 'n which is the top?

BARRY. Take it quietly, take it quietly, Darry.

DARRY (*resentfully*). Take it quietly? An' the time galloping by? I can't stand up on a chair 'n say to the sun, stand thou still there, over the meadow th' missus is mowing, can I?

BARRY. I know damn well you can't, but you're not going to expedite matters by rushing around in a hurry.

DARRY (*he has struggled into the overall*). Expedite matters! It doesn't seem to strike you that when you do things quickly, things are quickly done. Expedite matters! I suppose loitering to look at you lying on the broad of your back, jiggling your legs about, was one way of expediting matters; an' listening to you plucking curious sounds out of a mandolin, an' singing a questionable song, was another way of expediting matters?

BARRY. You pioneered me into doing the two of them yourself.

DARRY (*busy with the pot on the fire*). I pioneered you into doing them! Barry Derrill, there's such a thing in the world as a libel. You came strutting in with a mandolin under your arm, didn't you?

BARRY. I did, but——

DARRY. An' you sang your song.

BARRY. Yes, but——

DARRY. When you waltz'd in, I was doing calisthenics, wasn't I?

BARRY. I know you were; but all the same——

DARRY. An' you flung yourself down on the floor, and got yourself into a tangle trying to do them too, didn't you?

BARRY. Hold on a second——

DARRY. Now, I can't carry the conversation into a debate, for I have to get going. So if you can't give a hand, go, 'n let me do the things that have to be done, in an' orderly 'n quiet way.

BARRY. 'Course I'll give a hand—only waiting to be asked.

DARRY (*looking at the clock, suddenly*). Is the clock stopped?

BARRY (*taking up clock and putting it close to his ear*). There's no ticking, 'n it's hours slow.

DARRY. Lizzie again! Forgot to wind it. Give the key a few turns, Barry, an' put the hands on to half-past nine.

> (BARRY *starts to wind the clock.* DARRY *goes over to table, gets a basin of water, begins to wash the delf, humming to himself the air of the song,* "*Down where the bees are humming*". BARRY *winds and winds away, but no sign is given of a tightening of the spring inside. He looks puzzled, winds again, and is about to silently put the clock back where he found it, when* DARRY *turns and looks at him questioningly.*)

DARRY. You've broken the damn thing, have you?

BARRY. I didn't touch it.

DARRY. Didn't touch it? Amn't I after looking at you twisting an' tearing at it for nearly an hour? (*He comes over to* BARRY.) Show me that. (*He takes the clock from* BARRY *and opens the back, and the spring darts out.*) Didn't touch it. Oh,

154

for God's sake be more careful when you're handling things in this house! Dih dih dih. (*He pushes the spring back, and slaps the clock down on the dresser.*) You must have the hands of a gorilla, man. Here, come over 'n wipe while I wash.

> (*A slight pause while the two of them work at the delf.* DARRY *anxiously watches* BARRY, *who, being very near-sighted, holds everything he wipes close up to his spectacles.*)

DARRY (*suddenly*). Look out, look out, there— you're not leaving that jug on the table at all; you're depositing it in the air, man!

BARRY (*peering down at the table*). Am I? Don't be afraid, I won't let anything drop.

DARRY (*humming the song*). Dum dah de de dum da dee dee dum dah dee dee dee dah ah dum.

BARRY (*swinging his arm to the tune*). Down where the bees are hummin' an' the wild flowers gaily growing.

DARRY. Fine swing, you know. Dum dah dee dee dum dah dee dee dum dah dee dee dee dah ah dum.

BARRY (*swinging his arm*). Down where the bees are hummin'—

> (BARRY'S *arm sends the jug flying off the table on to the floor.*)

DARRY (*yelling*). You snaky-arm'd candle-power-ey'd elephant, look at what you're after doing!

BARRY (*heatedly*). It's only a tiny jug, anyhow, 'n you can hardly see the pieces on the floor!

DARRY (*just as heatedly*). An' if I let you do much more, they would soon be big enough to bury us! Sit down, sit down in the corner there; do nothing, say nothing, an', if I could, I'd put a safety curtain round you. For God's sake, touch nothing while I run out an' give the spuds to the pig.

> (DARRY *dashes over to the fire, whips the pot off, and runs out. He leaves the door open, and again the rattling whirr of a mowing machine can be heard.* BARRY *sits dejectedly in a corner. After a few moments a bump is heard outside, followed by a yell from* DARRY, *who, a second later, comes rushing madly in, a bloody handkerchief pressed to his nose. He flings himself flat on the floor on his back, elevating his nose as much as possible.*)

DARRY. Get me something cold to put down the back of my neck, quick!

BARRY (*frightened*). What the hell did you do to yourself?

156

THE END OF THE BEGINNING

DARRY. I didn't bend low enough when I was going in, 'n I gave myself such a, oh such a bang on my nose on the concrete. Get something cold, man, to shove down the back of my neck 'n stop the bleeding!

BARRY. Keep the nose sticking up in the air as high as you can. I don't know where to get something cold to shove down the back of your neck. I knew this rushing round wouldn't expedite matters.

DARRY (*with a moan of resentment as he hears "expedite matters"*). Oh, pull yourself together, man, 'n remember we're in the middle of an emergency.

BARRY. A little block of ice, now, would come in handy.

DARRY. A little——oh, a little block of ice! An' will you tell us where you're going to get a little block of ice? An', even if we had one, how could you fasten it down the back of my neck? Eh? Can't you answer——where are you going to get a block of ice?

BARRY. How the hell do I know where I'm going to get it?

DARRY. D'ye expect me to keep lying here till the winter comes?

> (*During this dialogue* BARRY *is moving round the room aimlessly, peering into*

> *drawers, rattling the delf on the dresser
> with his nose as he looks along the shelves.*)

DARRY (*as he hears the crockery rattling*). Mind, mind, or you'll break something. I must be losing a lot of blood, Barry, an' I won't be able to keep my nose sticking up in the air much longer. Can't you find anything?

BARRY. I can see nothing.

DARRY. Run upstairs 'n get the key of the big shed that's hanging on the wall, somewhere over the mantelpiece at the far end of the room. Go quick, man!

> (BARRY *runs upstairs, goes into room, comes
> out again, and looks down at* DARRY.)

DARRY (*up to him*). Did you get it?

BARRY. Where's the switch? It's as dark as pitch in there.

> (DARRY, *with a moan of exasperation, sits
> up, but immediately plunges down on his
> back again.*)

DARRY. Starts pumping out again the minute I sit up. (*To* BARRY) There's no switch in that room. We can't have a switch in every corner of the room just to suit you! You've only got to move down the centre of the room till you come to the fireplace; then brush your hand over the mantelpiece, along the wall, till you feel the key hanging there.

(BARRY *goes back into the room. After a few seconds' silence, there is a crash of falling crockery.* DARRY, *after a second of silent consternation, sits up with a jerk, but immediately plunges down on his back again.*)

DARRY (*sinking supine on the floor*). What has he done now; oh, what has he done now? (*Shouting up to* BARRY) Eh, you up there— what have you done now?

BARRY (*sticking his head out of door above*). Nothing much—the washhand-stand fell over.

DARRY (*angrily*). Nothing much. It sounded a hell of a lot, then. You're the kind of man if you're not chained up, 'll pull everything in the house asundher! Come down, come down, 'n stop down, or that delicate little hand of yours 'll smash everything in the house!

BARRY. My eyes are used to the darkness, now, 'n I can see. I'll get the key for you.

(*He goes back into the room, leaving* DARRY *speechless. After a few seconds, he comes out of the room in a sweat of fright and anger, one hand tightly clasped over the other. He rushes down the stairs, and begins to pull the things out of the chest of drawers, every other moment leaving off to clasp one hand over the other.*)

BARRY (*frantically*). Get your own key, get your own key. Half slaughtering myself for your sake! Why don't you keep your razor-blades in a safe place, an' not leave them scattered about in heaps all over the mantelpiece? Where is there a bit of old rag till I bind up my wounds? Get your own key yourself, I'm tellin' you.

DARRY. Amn't I nicely handicapped, wanting help an' having only the help of a half-blind man?

BARRY. D'ye know I'm nearly after mowing my fingers off with your blasted razor-blades? (*Coming near to* DARRY, *with a handkerchief in his hand, and showing the injured fingers to him.*) Look at them, uh, look at them—one looks as if only a thin thread of flesh was keeping it on. How am I going to play the mandolin now?

DARRY. You'd play it better if all your fingers were off.

BARRY (*keeping the wounded hand in the air, and holding out the handkerchief to* DARRY *with the other*). Here, get a grip of this 'n help me to bind up me wounds.

> (BARRY *kneels down beside the prostrate*
> DARRY, *who takes the handkerchief and*
> *proceeds to tie it round* BARRY'S *wounded*
> *fingers.*)

DARRY (*keeping his nose well up in the air*). You

give that an unexpected honour, if you call that
a wound!

>   (DARRY *ties the handkerchief round* BARRY's
>   *hand, who stands looking at it.*)

BARRY (*reflectively*). Won't be able to do much
for you with it now.

DARRY. It'll limit your capacity for breakin'
things.

>   (*A pause.*)

DARRY. Slip out, Barry, old son, 'n see if the
heifer's safe on the bank beside the house.

>   (BARRY *goes outside the door and stands
>   looking up towards the top of the house.
>   The light has been fading, and it is get-
>   ting dark. Again can be heard the
>   whirr of the mowing machine, and the
>   Town Hall clock strikes ten.*)

BARRY. I think I can hear her croppin' the
grass all right, but it doesn't seem wise to leave
her there 'n the dusk fallin'.

DARRY (*testily*). I can't do anything till this
bleeding stops, can I?

BARRY. The spuds are all scattered about here
where you let them fall when you were runnin' in.

DARRY (*moaning*). 'N can't you get the broom
'n sweep them up into a corner, 'n not be trampling them into the ground; you see the state
I'm in!

(BARRY *gets the broom and starts to sweep outside the door.*)

BARRY (*in to* DARRY). How's it now?

DARRY (*cautiously sitting up*). It's nearly stopped now, but I'll have to go cautious.

(BARRY, *sweeping with one hand, manages to bring the broom-handle into contact with the window, and breaks a pane. A silent pause.*)

BARRY (*as if he didn't know*). What's that, what's that?

DARRY (*in an agony of anger*). What's that, what's that! Can't you see, man, that you're after thrustin' the handle of the broom through one of the windows?

BARRY (*peering down at the hole in the window*). That's curious, now, for I never felt the handle touchin' the window; but there's a hole in it, right enough.

DARRY (*with angry mockery*). No, you wouldn't feel it touchin' it, either. A hole in it—of course there's a hole in it! My God Almighty, I've a destroyin' angel in the house!

BARRY. Well, not much use of lookin' at it now.

DARRY (*vehemently*). Oh come in, come in, come in, man. Didn't you hear the clock strikin' ten? I'll have to get goin' now.

(He gets up gingerly, feeling his nose, and still keeping it at a high angle.)

BARRY *(introducing another subject)*. Hadn't you better stable the heifer before you do anything?

DARRY *(violently)*. Haven't I to clean out the cowhouse first before I stable her, man? With your exercisin', 'n your singin', 'n your great 'n godly gift of expeditin' matters, I haven't made a bit of headway! I hadn't a chance to give her the graze she needs, so let her get all she can on the bank at the back of the house.

BARRY. Supposing she wanders to the edge of the bank 'n tumbles off?

DARRY. I don't know what to do about that.

BARRY. Couldn't you tie her to something?

DARRY *(angrily)*. There's nothing to tie her to, man.

BARRY. What about putting a rope down the chimney 'n tying it to something in the room?

DARRY *(after a few seconds' thought)*. That's a good idea, Barry. There's a rope outside, an' I'll sling one end round her neck, let the other end down the chimney, an' tie it to a chair. Wait here a second 'n get it when it comes down.

(DARRY rushes out. After a few moments his voice is heard faintly from above calling, "Hello, hello!" BARRY, *who*

has his head a little up the chimney, the smoke making him cough, answers, "Righto, let her come." *The rope comes down;* BARRY *catches the end and pulls it into the room.* DARRY *returns, and they tie the rope to a chair.*)

BARRY. Put the chair at the far end of the room, an' if the heifer wanders too far, we'll see the chair moving across the room.

DARRY (*with enthusiasm*). Now you're beginnin' to use your brains at last, Barry, me boy. (*He shifts the chair to the far end of the room.*) Now we can get goin' 'n get everything shipshape before the missus toddles back. Let's put on the light to see what we're doin'.

(*He snaps down the switch, but no light comes into the bulb.*)

DARRY (*annoyed*). Dih dih dih—must be the meter again.

(*He hurries into the lumber room, stepping over the rope.*)

BARRY (*speaking in to* DARRY). I wouldn't do much tamperin' with that.

DARRY (*inside room — emphatically*). Oh, I know what I'm doin'.

(DARRY *rushes out again, snaps down the switch, but no light comes.*)

DARRY (*irritably*). Must be the blasted bulb.

164

(*He rushes to a drawer.*)   There's a bulb here, somewhere, we've had for a long time, 'n never used.   (*He takes one from the drawer.*)   Here we are.   (*He pulls a chair to the centre of the room, stands on it, takes off the old bulb, and gives it to* BARRY.)   See if you can see anything wrong with it.

BARRY (*holding it to his nose*).   Can't see anything.

DARRY.   Leave it down, leave it down.

BARRY.   Sure the one you're fixing's the right voltage?

DARRY (*stopping to look at* BARRY).   Course it's the right voltage.   Why wouldn't it be the right voltage?

BARRY.   If it wasn't, it might fuse.

DARRY.   Fuse.   No fear of it fusing.   (*He starts to work again.*)

(*The chair to which the rope is tied begins to move across the floor.*)

BARRY (*startled*).   Look out, look out—the heifer's moving!

DARRY.   Catch hold of it, catch hold of it, before she disappears up the chimney!

(BARRY *catches the chair, but the strain is too much, and he is pulled along.* DARRY *jumps down off the chair, leaves the bulb on the table, catches hold of the rope, and helps* BARRY *to tug the chair back to the far end of the room.*)

DARRY. You sit on the chair, 'n then she can't move without our knowledge.

(BARRY *sits on the chair;* DARRY *mounts the chair again, and starts to fix the bulb. The chair begins to move with* BARRY *sitting on it.*)

BARRY (*excitedly*). Eh, quick again, get down, the heifer's movin'!

(DARRY *jumps down again, and the two of them pull the chair back to its place.*)

DARRY. The missus'll be back 'n nothin' done but damage.

(*He gets up again and fixes the bulb; there is a flash, and the room is darker than ever.*)

BARRY (*like a prophet*). I warned you, Darry; I saw it comin'.

DARRY (*forcibly*). What are you blatherin' about? We're no worse off than we were before we fixed it. There's a drum of oil in the lumber room, 'n if there's any left in it we can light the lamps. You light the one hangin' on the wall, while I see how we stand.

(*He runs into the lumber room.* BARRY *takes the lamp from the wall, removes the chimney, and tries to light the wick,*

166

but he can't see it, and holds the match anywhere but near the wick. DARRY *comes out of cellar.*)

DARRY (*jubilantly*). Plenty of oil in it. Aw, you're not holding the match within a mile of the wick, man. Show it to me, show it to me. (*He takes the match from* BARRY, *and lights the lamp.*)

DARRY. Out with you now, 'n get one of the old lamps you'll find on one of the shelves to the right in the shed at the back of the yard.

BARRY. How'll I see?

DARRY. Strike a match 'n look. You'll see them staring at you. I'll take a canful of oil from the drum to put in it when you bring it back, 'n then we'll have lashin's of light.

BARRY (*going out by door*). I know I won't be able to see.

(DARRY, *with a can that has a long snout on it, runs back into the lumber room.* BARRY *has left the door open, and the rattling whirr of the mowing machine can be heard again. There is a slight pause. Suddenly* DARRY *rushes out of the lumber room over to the open door.*)

DARRY (*shouting madly*). Barry, Barry, come here quick, man! I turned the key of the tap too much, 'n it slipped out of me hand into a heap of rubbish, 'n I can't turn off the cock, 'n I can't find the key in the dark. Come quick, man, or there won't be a drop of oil left in the drum!

> (*He rushes wildly back into the lumber room. Another slight pause. He rushes out again, with the drum in his arms, his thumb pressed to the tap outlet, and runs over to the door.*)

DARRY (*calling madly*). Eh, Barry, Barry, d'ye hear me callin' you, man? I won't be able to keep this oil in much longer. Have you fallen asleep, or what?

> (*There is heard outside a rattle, followed by a crash of falling pots, tins, and tools; then a dead silence for a moment.*)

DARRY (*staggering against the wall*). Aw, Mother o' God, what's he after doin' now!

BARRY (*outside, in a loud voice of great distress*). Darry, oh Darry, I'm after nearly destroyin' meself! Where's the doorway?—I can't see!

DARRY (*going over and standing in the doorway*). Here, here, man; no, to the left. (*As* BARRY *staggers in, dusty and frightened*) What ruin are you after causin' now?

BARRY (*moaningly*). I'm after gettin' an awful shock!

168

DARRY (*appealingly*). Pull yourself together, for God's sake man, 'n tell us what's happened.

BARRY (*as he sinks down on a chair*). The blasted lamps were on top of the top shelf; there was nothing to stand on; I had to climb up on the shelves, and climbing up, the shelves 'n all that was on them came down on top of me!

> (DARRY *goes over and rests the drum in the sink, his hand still pressed over the outlet of the tap.*)

DARRY. 'N why did you climb the shelves? What did you want to do that for? Couldn't you see, you sap, that they weren't fixed well in the wall? Why did you insist on climbing the shelves?

BARRY. I was just tryin' to expedite matters.

DARRY (*with a wail*). Tryin' to expedite matters. Oh, there'll be a nice panorama of ruin in front of Lizzie when she comes back!

BARRY. 'N me spectacles were sent flyin' when the shelves fell.

DARRY. 'N why didn't you grab them before they fell to the ground?

BARRY (*hotly*). How could I grab them 'n they fallin', when I was fallin' too!

DARRY (*impatiently*). Well, get the lamp then, 'n look for the lost key in the lumber room.

BARRY. 'N maybe let it fall, 'n set the house on fire?

DARRY (*woefully*). Oh amn't I in a nice predic— The chair, the chair—the heifer's movin'!

> (*The chair to which the rope is tied begins to move across the floor.* BARRY *catches it, tugs manfully, but he is carried on towards the fireplace.*)

BARRY (*anxiously*). Give us a hand, give us a hand, or I'll be up the chimney!

> (DARRY *leaving the drum, runs over to* BARRY'S *side, grips the rope in front of* BARRY, *and, to get a safer hold, takes the rope off the chair and puts it round him under his arms. With great pulling, they get the rope a little back. The oil flows from the drum into the sink unnoticed.*)

DARRY (*panting*). Keep a strain, or we'll be up the chimney!

BARRY. How'm I goin' to get home to-night without me spectacles?

DARRY (*loudly*). Keep a sthrain on her, man, keep a sthrain on her; we have to get this straightened out first, before we can brood over your spectacles!

BARRY (*suddenly noticing the oil drum*). The oil, the oil!

THE END OF THE BEGINNING

(*He lets go of the rope, and runs over to the oil drum.* DARRY *disappears up the chimney.*)

BARRY (*lifting the drum and shaking it*). Not a drop left in it, not a single drop! What're we goin' to do n——

(*He turns and sees that* DARRY *has disappeared.*)

LIZZIE (*speaking outside in a voice of horror*). The heifer, the heifer!

DARRY (*calling out*). Lizzie, Lizzie!

(LIZZIE *rushes in as* DARRY *falls down the chimney. He crawls out from the fireplace on his hands and knees, and halts there, exhausted and sooty.*)

LIZZIE (*horrified*). What in the Name of God has happened?

DARRY (*to* LIZZIE). Now you see the result of havin' your own way! Why the hell didn't you hold on to the rope when you took it off the heifer, so that I wouldn't come down with a bump?

LIZZIE. How'd I know you were hangin' on the other end?

DARRY (*indignantly*). You didn't know—my God, woman, can you do nothin' right!

CURTAIN

MUSIC FOR SONG IN
"THE END OF THE BEGINNING"

DOWN WHERE THE BEES ARE HUMMING

One sum-mer eve a hand-some man met a hand-some maid-en stroll-ing, Down where the bees were hum-ming and the wild flowers gai-ly grow-ing; Said she we'll sit down here a while, all self-ish thoughts con-troll-ing, Down where the bees are hum-ming and the wild flowers gai-ly grow-ing: Said she we'll med-i-tate on things, things high and ed-i-fy-ing, How all things live and have their day and end their day by dy-ing. He put his hand on her white breast and mur-mured life is try-ing, Down where the bees are hum-ming and the wild flowers gai-ly grow-ing.

A POUND ON DEMAND

A Sketch in One Act

CHARACTERS

A GIRL, *in charge of Pimblico Sub-Post Office.*
JERRY, a working man.
SAMMY, another.
A POLICEMAN.

SCENE

A Sub-Post Office on a late autumn evening.

SCENE: *A Post Office.   There is a counter to the right which comes out for about four yards, turning at right angles, and running to the back. That part of the counter facing front is railed, and has in the centre a small, bracketed window for selling stamps.   Above the window is a card on which is the word* STAMPS.   *There is a swing-door in the centre at the back.   To the right of the door a window having the words* POST OFFICE *on it to face towards the street. To the left is a table-ledge for the convenience of those who want to write letters, telegrams, fill in forms, or make out postal orders.   Blotting-paper, quill pens, inkwells are on the ledge. Above ledge at back a telephone booth. Notices, such as, Save Saving Certificates, and Saving Certificates will Save You! Buy by Telephone; Post Often and Post Early; Cardinal Virtues: Temperance, Prudence, Fortitude, Payment of Income Tax.*

Behind the counter, sitting on a high stool beside a desk, is a GIRL *sorting and examining*

175

*documents, and doing the routine work of a Post
Office.   Behind counter, on the left, a door.   It
is six o'clock or so in the evening of an autumn
day; the sun is low in the sky, and his red light
is flooding in through the window.*

The swing-door suddenly opens and JERRY,
*pressing his body against the door to keep it open,
while he holds* SAMMY, *who is drunk, steady
with his right hand, appears to view with an
anxious and hopeful look on his face.   JERRY
is dressed in cement-soiled working clothes, and
his trousers are bound under the knees with
cords.   He is about forty years of age.   His
friend,* SAMMY, *is a workman too, and is
dressed in the same way.   JERRY wears a large
tweed cap, and* SAMMY *wears a brown trilby
much the worse for wear.   SAMMY is in a state
of maudlin drunkenness, and his reddish face is
one wide, silly grin.*

JERRY (*holding on to* SAMMY *and calling in to the*
GIRL). Yous do Post Office Savin's Bank business here, don't you, miss?

> (*Before the* GIRL *has time to reply,* SAMMY
> *lurches away from the door, pulling* JERRY
> *with him, and the door swings shut again.
> The* GIRL *looks round, but sees only the
> swinging door.   A pause.   The door*

opens again, and JERRY, *holding* SAMMY *with a firmer grip, appears and speaks in to the* GIRL.)

JERRY (*to the* GIRL). Savin's Bank's business's's done here, miss, isn't it?

(SAMMY *lurches again, pulling* JERRY *with him, so that the door again swings shut. Again the* GIRL *looks round and sees only the swinging door. She keeps her eyes on it. A pause. The door opens again and the two men appear, this time with* JERRY *behind* SAMMY *pushing him, and looking round him as he speaks in to the* GIRL.)

JERRY (*looking round* SAMMY *as he speaks in to the* GIRL). Savin's bank business's's done here, isn't it, miss?

GIRL (*suspiciously*). Yes.

JERRY (*exultingly to* SAMMY). I told you, Sammy, this is a Post Office where Savin's Bank business's's done. In we go.

SAMMY (*looking round vacantly*). Where?

JERRY. In there, in here, can't you see? We're in port, Sammy—Post Office where Savin's Bank business's's done.

SAMMY (*vacantly*). Where?

JERRY (*appealingly*). Aw, pull yourself together, Sammy. Remember the mission we're

on; don't let a fella down now. Remember what
we want.

SAMMY (*vacantly*). Want nothin'.

JERRY (*irritably*). Try to remember, man—
pound on demand—remember?

SAMMY (*stiffening*). Pound on demand, wanna
pound on demand.

JERRY. Why're you sayin' you want nothin',
then? Don't make a fool of me when it comes
to the push. You've only to sign a form—the
young lady'll give it to you.

SAMMY. Sign no form; don't wanna form.

JERRY (*irritably*). You can't get your pound,
man, till you sign a form. That's the way they
do Savin's Bank business's, see? Sign a form
askin' a pound on demand, 'n hand it over to the
young lady, see?

SAMMY. Wanna drink.

JERRY. You've no money for a dhrink. Can't
get a dhrink till you get your pound on demand.
(*Guiding* SAMMY *over to the counter.*) Thry to keep
your composure while we're doing the business.

(*The pair come to the counter.*)

JERRY (*in a wheedling way to the* GIRL). He
wants a pound on demand, missie; (*to* SAMMY)
don't you, Sammy—a pound on demand? (*To
the* GIRL) Give's the form, missie, till he pops
his name down on it.

GIRL (*to* SAMMY—*ignoring* JERRY). What can I do for you, sir?

SAMMY (*vacantly*). Wha'?

> (*A stoutish* WOMAN *of about forty comes in by the door with a minor kind of a rush, and hurries over to the counter. She stares for a moment at the two men.*)

WOMAN (*to the* GIRL). If I wrote a letter 'n posted it to catch the seven fifty-nine P.M. collection, would it get to Tarraringapatam on Friday before twelve fifty-four in the afternoon, please?

GIRL (*trying to collect her wits together*). What collection, madam?

WOMAN (*stiffly*). I said the seven fifty-nine P.M. collection, I think.

JERRY (*impatiently*). Gie's the little form, missie.

SAMMY (*drunkenly breaking into song*). Jush a song at twilight, when the lights 're slow——

JERRY (*remonstrating*). Eh, eh, there, Sammy!

SAMMY (*a little subdued*). 'N the flickerin' shadowish softly——

JERRY (*emphatically*). Eh, Sammy, eh!

SAMMY (*ending it softly*). Come 'n go.

GIRL (*to the* WOMAN). The destination of the letter, madam, please?

WOMAN. Tarraringapatam.

GIRL. Where exactly is that place or locality, madam?

SAMMY. Nex' parish but one t' ourish.

WOMAN (*indignantly*, *to* SAMMY). Keep your funny remarks to yourself, please. (*To the* GIRL) Tarraringapatam's in the most southern part of Burma.

JERRY (*to the* GIRL). Fork over the form for the pound on demand, will you, missie?

GIRL (*to* JERRY). One minute, please.

SAMMY (*hammering on counter with his hand*). A pound en deman', wanna pound en deman'.

WOMAN (*to the* GIRL). Will a letter posted to catch the seven fifty-nine get to Tarraringapatam on Friday before twelve fifty-four in the afternoon?

GIRL. I'm afraid I couldn't say, madam.

JERRY (*briskly*, *to the* WOMAN). Young lady doesn't know. (*To the* GIRL) Pound on demand form, miss.

WOMAN (*indignantly*, *to* JERRY). Be good enough, sir, to confine your attention to your own business, will you? (*To the* GIRL) Will you find out?

JERRY (*to the* WOMAN). You can't be let monopolize the time 'n attention of an office for the use of the public at large, can you?

SAMMY (*briskly*). Ish she tryin' to shtir up trouble, or wha'?

WOMAN (*to* SAMMY). I'm making an ordinary enquiry at a public office, and I will not tolerate interference.

GIRL (*who has been running her finger along a list of names of places hanging on a card behind the counter*). What name again, please?

WOMAN (*with dignity*). Tarraringapatam.

GIRL (*looking at the list*). Not on the list, madam.

JERRY (*ironically*). Bus stop in the jungle, miss.

WOMAN. It must be there.

GIRL (*to the* WOMAN). Not on the list. (*To* SAMMY) What can I do for you, sir?

JERRY (*confidentially*). Just wants a pound on demand, miss.

GIRL (*sharply, to* JERRY). Let the gentleman speak for himself. (*To* SAMMY) What is it, please?

SAMMY. Ish she tryin' to shtir up trouble, or wha'?

JERRY (*loudly, to* SAMMY). Young lady's askin' if you want a pound on demand.

SAMMY (*wakening up a little*). Yeh, wha'? Wanna pound on demand, yeh.

JERRY (*briskly*). Give's the form, 'n I'll get him to sling his name down, missie.

A POUND ON DEMAND

GIRL (*to* SAMMY). Can I have your bank-book, please?

JERRY (*briskly*). Bank-book, bank-book, Sammy; young lady wants the bank-book.

(SAMMY *looks vacantly at the* GIRL *and at* JERRY.)

JERRY (*briskly*). Get a move on. (*He puts a hand in* SAMMY'S *breast-pocket.*) Bank-book, bank-book, Sammy, me son; young lady wants bank-book.

(*He takes the book from* SAMMY'S *pocket, and hands it to the* GIRL.)

GIRL (*to* WOMAN, *who is standing beside the counter*). Sorry, madam, but I can't tell you what you want to know—the name's not on the list. (*She looks at the bank-book* JERRY *has given to her.*) Which is Mr. Adams?

JERRY (*gaily indicating his friend*). This is him, miss, all alive 'n full of beans.

SAMMY (*delightedly*). Jusht a song at twilight when the lights aresh slow——

JERRY (*interrupting*). Shush—young lady doesn't like singing in her office, Sammy.

SAMMY (*drunkenly*). Sammy doesn't care about any young ladyish; don't care 'bout offish or young ladyish.

WOMAN (*going over indignantly to ledge to write her letter*). A finely appointed Post Office, I

182

must say, that can't give you even a hint about
the commonest postal regulation!

> (*The* GIRL *slowly gets a form and reluc-
> tantly hands it out towards* SAMMY, *but*
> JERRY *takes it out of her hand, and hur-
> ries* SAMMY *over to the writing-ledge
> opposite.*)

GIRL (*warningly*). The depositor must sign
himself; and his signature must correspond
with that in the book.

> (*The* WOMAN *is writing her letter, and is
> taking up a great deal of space.   She is
> right in the middle of the ledge with
> writing materials spread round on each
> side of her.   JERRY leads* SAMMY *to the
> space on her right, looks at it, then leads*
> SAMMY *round to the space on her left.*)

JERRY. Now you've only just to gather the
pen into your mit 'n slap down the old name on
to the form.

> (JERRY *spreads the form on the ledge, gets a
> quill pen and puts it into* SAMMY'S *hand,
> who lets it fall to the floor.*)

JERRY (*with irritation, as he picks it up, and
places it again in* SAMMY'S *hand*). Try to keep a
grip on it, man, 'n don't be spillin' it all over the
place.   (SAMMY *grips it like a sword.*)   Aw, not
that way.   Don't go to the opposite extreme.

(*Arranging pen.*)   Nice 'n lightly between the finger 'n thumb.   That way, see?   (*Speaking over to the* GIRL.)   He's not used to this kind of thing, miss, but he'll be all right in a minute.

SAMMY (*standing still and looking vacantly at the wall*). Wanna poun' on demand.

JERRY (*encouragingly*). Go on, bend your back 'n write your name.   (*To the* WOMAN *who is writing her letter.*)   Mind movin' over as far as you can, ma'am, to give him room to write his name—he wants a pound on demand?

> (*The* WOMAN *looks indignant, but moves a little away.* SAMMY *bends down, gets the pen to the paper, slips and slides along the ledge, nearly knocking the* WOMAN *down.*)

JERRY (*in dismay*). Aw, Sammy, eh, eh. Look at the form, man.   Can't you keep your balance for a second?

WOMAN (*indignantly*). This is a nice way to be scattered about, writing an important letter to Tarraringapatam!   (*To the* GIRL) Aren't you going to exercise a little control here, please?

JERRY (*to the* WOMAN). He's sawl right, he's sawl right, ma'am.

WOMAN (*angrily*). No, it's not all right; it's anything but all right.   (*Violently, to* SAMMY) Remember you're in a Post Office, sir!

SAMMY (*with drunken indignation*). Posht Off-ish! What's a Posht Offish? Haven't to take me shoes from off me feet in a Posht Offish, have I?

JERRY (*soothingly*). It's sawl right. No one wants you to take your shoes from off your feet. Here, lean on the ledge till I get a new form.

(*He puts* SAMMY *leaning against the ledge and goes over to get another form.*)

SAMMY (*meandering over to the* WOMAN). Shuh want me to take me shoes from offish me feet?

JERRY (*to the* GIRL). Slip us another form, missie.

SAMMY (*close to the* WOMAN—*emphatically*). Shuh hear me talkin' to you? Shuh want me to take me shoish from off me feet?

JERRY (*impatiently to the* GIRL). Give's the form, miss, before he begins to get lively.

GIRL (*busy at work*). Oh, just a minute. I gave you one a moment ago.

SAMMY (*close to the* WOMAN). You push off, ma'am, please; thish plaish is occupied. Have to write me namish; need spaish; wanna pound on demand. (*The* WOMAN *ignores him.*) Push off when you're warned, can't you? Thish plaish ish occupied.

JERRY (*speaking over to* SAMMY *from the counter*). Eh, eh, Sammy, there, control yourself, man. (*To the* GIRL) Hurry up, miss.

A POUND ON DEMAND

SAMMY (*more emphatically, as the* WOMAN *ignores him*). Shuh hear me talkin' to you? Told you I wanted spaish. Push off, now—this plaish is occupied.

JERRY (*over to* SAMMY, *in a warning voice*). Sammy!

WOMAN (*indignantly to* SAMMY). How dare you tell me to push off? I'll have you know this is a public office, and I am engaged in important business.

SAMMY (*aggressively*). Shuh don't want a pound on demanish, so push off before I call the polish.

JERRY (*facing towards the* GIRL). Calm, Sammy, calm.

> (SAMMY *pushes the* WOMAN *as she is writing her letter, but she indignantly pushes back, and he finds it hard to keep his feet. He recovers and returns to the charge, pushes her again, but she pushes him more violently than before, sending him more than half-way towards the door; by a great effort he recovers and staggers back to the* WOMAN *with a look of determination on his face.*)

JERRY (*to the* GIRL, *as* SAMMY *is staggering about —which* JERRY *does not see*). For God's sake, give's a form, missie.

A POUND ON DEMAND

SAMMY (*pushing the* WOMAN). I have you taped, me lassie; wanta wash what'r we doin': I have you taped, but I'll block you, me lassie!

> (*He pushes the* WOMAN, *who pushes him back; he tries to recover, but she follows him up, and pushes again so that* SAMMY *staggers to the door, hits it, the door opens,* SAMMY *staggers out into the street, and the door closes again. The* WOMAN *goes back to the writing of her letter.*)

JERRY (*who is ignorant of* SAMMY'S *disappearance, rapping impatiently on the counter*). Eh miss, missie, the form, miss, eh, the form, missie.

GIRL (*impatiently slapping down a form on the counter*). That's the last you'll get.

JERRY (*combatively*). Oh, don't get too cocky, miss, for, after all, you're only a servant to the public. (*Tapping his chest*) It's the like of me that pays your wages. You're just here to serve the interests of the public, so don't get too cocky.

GIRL (*tartly*). I don't want any impertinence, please.

JERRY (*hotly*). You'll do what's here to do accordin' to regulations. I wonder what'd happen if I sent in a chit of a complaint to the Postmaster-General?

187

(*He turns round to go over to the writing-ledge and finds that* SAMMY *has disappeared.*)

JERRY (*staring round in bewilderment*). Where's he gone? Eh, where did Sammy go? (*He runs over to the* WOMAN.) Why the hell didn't you keep an eye on him when you knew he had a few up?

(*He rushes to the door, pushes it open and runs out.*)

WOMAN (*to the* GIRL). Nice pair of drunken scoundrels. What are the police doing?

(*The door swings open and* JERRY *enters, dragging* SAMMY *in after him.*)

JERRY (*indignantly, to the* GIRL). Eh, will you speak to that lady over there, 'n keep her from interferin' with people transactin' public business?

(*He leads* SAMMY *back to the writing-ledge, spreads the form on the ledge for him, and carefully places a pen in his hand.*)

SAMMY (*as he is being led over*). Have that lasshie taped; thash lasshie over there, have her taped, so I have.

JERRY (*placing the pen in* SAMMY'S *hand*). Get your mit goin', Sammy, get your mit goin'. (SAMMY *does not stir.*) Aw, get down to it, man.

SAMMY. Can't bend.

A POUND ON DEMAND

JERRY. Why can't you bend?

SAMMY. Can't bend, can't stand; wanna chair.

JERRY (*impatiently*). Hold on tight, then, while I get you one. Hold tight, now.

> (SAMMY *grips the writing-ledge grimly, as he stares over at the* WOMAN *who is writing at the other end.* JERRY *runs to the counter, acting and speaking so impetuously that the* GIRL *does what is asked of her before she realizes what is happening.*)

JERRY (*rapidly to the* GIRL). The stool, missie, a lend of the stool; he can write his name safer sittin'; quick, missie!

> (*The* GIRL *hands over a high stool,* JERRY *runs over to* SAMMY *with the stool, helps* SAMMY *to sit on it, settles the form, and again puts the pen in his hand.* SAMMY *protrudes his tongue, and seems to find his coat in the way.*)

JERRY. Oul coat in the way, eh? Take it off, then, so's it won't clog your movements; young lady won't mind.

> (*After a good deal of pulling,* SAMMY, *with the help of* JERRY, *gets off his coat.*)

WOMAN (*sarcastically, staring at the pair*). Why don't you pull down the blinds and keep the light from hurting his eyes?

(SAMMY *gives a violent movement of anger,*
sweeping pen, ink, and form to the
ground. Holding precariously to the
ledge, he tilts his seat, slides over
towards the WOMAN, *and brings his face*
as close to hers as possible.)

SAMMY (*angrily, to the* WOMAN). Thish ish a
Post Offish, see? No one allowed interfere
with men hash businish to do. Wasn't reared
yesterday, 'n I have you taped, me lasshie!

JERRY (*indignantly, to the* WOMAN). Whyja
go 'n cause a commotion just as the man was
doin' nicely? You've no right to interfere
with men transactin' public business. (*Over
to the* GIRL) See that, miss, see the way she
interfered the minute the man was just doin'
nicely?

GIRL (*calmly*). I didn't see the lady interfering
in any way.

JERRY (*indignantly*). Well, if you hadda had
your eyes open, you'd ha seen it. There
doesn't seem to be any proper conthrol in the
place at all.

(*While* JERRY *is speaking, the* GIRL *goes to*
the telephone, dials a number and listens.
JERRY *helps* SAMMY *back to his original*
position on the stool.)

GIRL (*at the telephone*). Hello; Pimblico Post

Office speaking; send down one of your little
boys, will you? Yes, at once, please.

> (*She replaces the receiver and stands
> watching the two men, glancing, now
> and again, at the door.*)

JERRY (*when he has settled* SAMMY). Now don't
fall asundher any more, for God's sake. (*To the*
WOMAN) 'N no more of your condescendin'
remarks, please, see?

WOMAN (*vehemently*). One word more from
either of you, 'n I'll go straight out 'n bring in
a policeman!

> (*There are a few moments' dead silence.*)

SAMMY (*breaking out excitedly*). Ja hear what
she said? Ja hear? Bring a policeman in.
That's what we get for trustin' people. What
do I care for the poleish? Speak up, Jerry, 'n
be a man—do I or do I not care for the poleish?

JERRY (*soothingly*). No, never; everyone who
knows Sammy, knows that.

SAMMY. Not if they were round me in dozens
—do I or do I not?

JERRY. Not a word, Sammy, not a word; we
rest silent about them things.

SAMMY. Not a word. We don't rush round
tellin' things; but we know, don't we, Jerry?

JERRY. Not a word. Don't let your nerves
get jangled now. Slip your name down.

SAMMY. Not another word. Poleeish! Do I or do I not care for the poleeish—you know, Jerry?

JERRY. Not a word—go on, get your name down.

SAMMY (*excitedly*). Let her send for the poleeish! Wouldn't be long till they didn't know what was happenin'. Poleeish to the right of me, 'n to the left of me, 'n nothing left of them in the end but silver buttons for souvenirs!

JERRY. Rags, bones, 'n buttons, wha'? Go on—slip your name down.

> (*The door opens and a huge* POLICEMAN *enters. He walks slowly in, goes over to the counter, looks at the* GIRL, *who points to the two men; the* POLICEMAN *nods knowingly.*)

SAMMY (*leaning over towards the* WOMAN). We often plastered the roads with policeman, 'n left them thryin' out how they were going to get themselves together again!

WOMAN (*scornfully*). Oh, you did, didja?

SAMMY (*mockingly, to the* WOMAN). Yes, we did, didn' we; we did did did didja, didn' we!

POLICEMAN (*coming over and standing near the two men*). Now, then, do what you have to do, 'n go about your business.

A POUND ON DEMAND

(The two men look round and see the
POLICEMAN. *They stare at him for a
few moments, and then turn their faces
away, fixing their attention on the form.
There is a dead silence for a time, for the
near presence of a* POLICEMAN *is a great
discomfort and very disconcerting.)*

JERRY *(almost in a whisper).* Just there on the
line, Sammy. Samuel, first name, see? Lead
off with a big ess. A big ess, man, a big ess.
Shape it into a big ess—capital ess—don't you
know what a capital ess is? Here, I'll show
you—give us a hold of the pen for a minute.

(JERRY *takes the pen from* SAMMY *and
makes the necessary correction, and returns the pen to* SAMMY.)

JERRY. There y'are now. No, on ahead,
cautious: a, m, u—I think—yes, u, double e, l
—no, one e 'n two double ells—good God,
what am I sayin'—only one double ell, only one
double ell, man! You're not listenin' to me,
Sammy. There's nothin' to prevent you doin'
it right, if you'll only listen. You've nearly a
dozen of ells down. Show it to me for a second.

*(He takes the pen and removes roughly the
unnecessary letters.)*

JERRY *(warningly).* Now the next name,
Adams; 'n make the letthers a little smaller, or

193

you'll be a mile away from the form before the last one comes in sight.

SAMMY (*in a weary voice*). Aw, I've had enough.

JERRY. You're too far ahead to give up now, man. T'other name, now. A big a for a start. Not as big as an elephant, now—you know what an ordinary capital A is. Oh, why did you let your hand slip? It'll have to do now. (*Turning and winking at the* POLICEMAN) He's got a few up, but he's sawl right. (*To* SAMMY) Now a little d, 'n a little u, 'n a little— wait a minute—I'm gettin' a little confused—a little m, a little n, 'n a little ess—a little ess, man! Now, come on, 'n we'll give it to the young lady.

WOMAN (*mockingly, to* JERRY). The poor man'll need a long rest, now.

(JERRY *helps* SAMMY *off the stool, and links him over to the counter, both of them trying to appear as if they were indifferent to the presence of the* POLICEMAN. *He hands over the form to the* GIRL, *who examines it, and looks at the name in the bank-book.*)

JERRY (*humming, and trying to look unconcerned*). Rum tum tiddley um tum, parley voo; rum tum tiddley um tum, parley voo; rum tum——

A POUND ON DEMAND

GIRL (*interrupting* JERRY's *humming*). Couldn't give you a pound on demand with this signature. The signature on the form doesn't correspond with the signature in the bank-book in any way.

JERRY. It's his writin', isn't it, miss? An' both of the names is Adamsususes, aren't they?

GIRL. They don't correspond. Sorry; but I can't let you have the money. I don't even know that the gentleman is really Mr. Adams.

JERRY (*wild*). Didja ever hear such consequential nonsense! (*To* SAMMY) She says you're not Mr. Adams. (*To the* GIRL) Of course he's Mr. Adams. Who else could he be, only Mr. Adams? Isn't he known all over the district where he lives, woman?

GIRL. Why, then, didn't he go to the Post Office in his own district?

JERRY (*impatiently*). Because it's too busy an office, 'n we decided to come to a place where he could do what he wanted to do in comfort, 'n fill in his name at his ease.

GIRL (*with decision*). I'm sorry; but I can't let the gentleman have the money.

JERRY (*horrified*). 'N what's he goin' to do, then?

GIRL. Better call back again to-morrow, or the next day.

JERRY. He wants the money now, girl.

GIRL. I can't give it to him.

JERRY (*to* SAMMY). She says she won't give you the pound on demand.

SAMMY. Wanna pound on demand.

JERRY (*to the* GIRL). Hear what the depositor says? He's gotta get it.

SAMMY. I've gotta get it.

JERRY (*to* SAMMY). Of course you have. After the agony of gettin' things ship-shape, we're not goin' to stand any denial of our rights.

POLICEMAN (*coming near*). Hasn't the young lady said she can't give it to you? So go on home, now, like decent men, an' forget all about it.

JERRY (*to the* POLICEMAN). The man has gotta get his money, hasn't he?

SAMMY (*dreamily*). 'Course I've gotta get it.

POLICEMAN (*importantly*). Since he hasn't complied with the necessary preliminaries, he isn't entitled to withdraw his pound.

JERRY (*indignantly*). The only preliminary was the signin' of his name, wasn't it? 'N he signed his name, didn't he? Y'awl seen him signin' his name, didn't you? (*A pause.*) Are yous all afraid to speak—did yous, or didn't yous?

POLICEMAN. G'on now, g'on. (*To* JERRY)

Y'ought to see that your comrade's incapable of discretion in withdrawin' anything from a Government corporation. G'on, now, like decent men.

JERRY (*appealingly*). He wants that pound special, I'm tellin' you. (*To* SAMMY) Don't you, Sammy?

SAMMY (*dreamily*). I gotta get it.

JERRY (*to the* POLICEMAN). Hear that? Mind you, it's a serious thing to keep a man from gettin' his private property.

POLICEMAN (*a little angry*). Here, g'on the pair of yous, before I lose me temper! You've been shown every leniency; so go home, now, like sensible, decent men, before I lose me temper.

JERRY. Give us back the bank-book, then.

GIRL. Mr. Adams might lose it—I'll post it on to him to-morrow.

JERRY (*frightened*). He doesn't want you to post it. He wants it now—don't you, Sammy?

SAMMY (*wearily*). I've gotta get it.

POLICEMAN (*peremptorily*). Now go on home, like decent men, before I have to resort to exthremes. Go on 'n sleep over it, 'n to-morrow, after a wash 'n brush up, you'll be able to apply for your pound in an ordherly 'n sensible manner.

JERRY (*wildly*). 'N are we goin' to get nothin' out of all our efforts? Mind you, there'll be throuble about this.

POLICEMAN (*roughly*). Ay, it'll start now if the two of yous don't bounce off 'n be well on your way home in a minute. (*He gently pushes them towards the door.*) G'on, now, you know your way.

JERRY (*sorrowfully*). 'N we thravelled miles to find this quiet place, so that he could sign his name in peace.

WOMAN (*mockingly, as they go out*). Isn't it a pity to disappoint the poor little children.

SAMMY (*as they go out*). I've gotta get it.

> (*They go slowly and sorrowfully out. The* POLICEMAN *holds the door open for them, and closes it when they have gone. The* WOMAN *goes over to the counter with her letter.*)

WOMAN. Registered, please.

> (*The* GIRL *takes the letter, registers it, and hands receipt to the* WOMAN, *who puts it in her bag and goes out.*)

GIRL (*to the* POLICEMAN). Glad you hunted that pair of money philanderers out of the place.

POLICEMAN (*taking her hand into his as he reclines over the counter*). You're lookin' fit 'n fair 'n sweet 'n rosy to-day, so you are.

GIRL (*coyly*). Am I?

A POUND ON DEMAND

POLICEMAN (*shyly*). Yes, y'are, so y'are.

> (*The door opens a little way then closes
> again. The* POLICEMAN *lets go the* GIRL'S
> *hand and stands stiff, while the* GIRL
> *pretends to be busy with a document.*)

GIRL. Thought that was someone.

POLICEMAN. Same here. (*He takes her hand
again.*) Y'are, really, lookin' fit 'n fair 'n sweet
'n rosy to-day, so y'are.

GIRL (*archly*). Am I?

> (*The door suddenly swings open again, and
> SAMMY appears, with JERRY steadying
> him from behind. They stand in the
> doorway, keeping it from closing with
> their shoulders. The POLICEMAN and
> the GIRL move away from each other.*)

JERRY (*encouragingly to* SAMMY). Go on,
give them your ultimatum : tell them straight that
you're goin' to write to the Postmaster-General
before you settle down for the night. Go on,
now—give them your ultimatum!

> (*They both come in towards the centre of the
> office.*)

SAMMY (*pointing a finger towards the* GIRL *and the*
POLICEMAN, *which shakes and wanders from the
floor to the ceiling as he points*). I have yous taped,
two of yous 'n Postmasterzheneral! Taped,
well taped I have, Postmasterzheneral!

JERRY (*trying to cover up* SAMMY'S *vagueness*).
Mr. Adams, the depositor, has made up his mind
to send a bitther complaint to the Postmaster-
General about the way he's been shunted about
by public servants durin' his application for a
pound on demand. (*To* SAMMY) Haven't you,
Mr. Adams?

SAMMY. I'm tellin' them, once for all, I've
gotta get it.

JERRY. There y'are, you see; can't say I didn't
warn you. Somebody will be made to sit up for
this.

POLICEMAN (*loudly and ominously*). If the pair of
yous aren't gone for good in two ticks of the
clock, yous'll spend the night in a place that'll
give the two of you plenty of time to complain to
the Postmaster-General. (*He makes a move towards them.*) Be off, I'm tellin' yous, yourselves
an' your pound on demand!

> (*The two men are frightened by his move
> towards them, and* JERRY *manœuvres*
> SAMMY *swiftly to the door, and both of
> them leave as quick as* SAMMY *can travel.*)

JERRY (*as they reach the door*). Somebody'll be
made to sit up for this, I'm tellin' you!

> (*As the doors swing shut, they open again
> partly to show* JERRY'S *face glaring
> savagely into the office.*)

A POUND ON DEMAND

JERRY (*shouting in from the partly opened door*). That's the last penny of our money the Government'll ever get from us!

(*His face disappears, the door swings shut, and the curtain comes down.*)

CURTAIN

Printed in Great Britain by R. & R. CLARK, LIMITED, *Edinburgh.*